LYING DOWN WITH DOGS

WITH

DOGS

Natalie Pantaleo

The Awakened Press
www.theawakenedpress.com

For information about special discounts for bulk purchases, please contact The Awakened Press at books@theawakenedpress.com.

The Awakened Press can bring authors to your live event. For more information or to book an event contact books@theawakenedpress.com or visit our website at www.theawakenedpress.com.

Cover and book design by Kurt A. Dierking II

Image of woman on cover is part of a larger portrait by artist Barbara Hyman of Long Island, N.Y.: barbarahymanart.com

Printed in the United States of America
First The Awakened Press trade paperback edition

ISBN: 979-8-9860377-1-4

6/30/05
Aunt Jerry
Here's to the
rich experiences
life gives us:
Natalee

LYING DOWN WITH DOGS

Natalie Pantaleo

The Awakened Press

Contents

Dedicated to the souls of two loving, steadfast, and resilient women who always maintained a sense of humor, my grandmothers:

Mary (Bruno) Vanore, July 1, 1913 – August 11, 1995
Josie (Troilo) Pantaleo, March 3, 1912 – July 30, 1997

And to another old soul and the bravest girl I know,
my truly lovely daughter, Madison.
Never give up dreaming, Madi.
Always try to put faith in the realm of untold possibilities;
if you can visualize it, you can have it.

You Should Write This Down

I stared at the Tavern restaurant across the street through a window in Rosie's cafe. It seemed only a pane of glass and a municipal parking lot separated me from my first night there eleven years before. I could just as well have parked my old Hyundai hatchback in the lot, grabbed my apron and wine opener from the passenger seat, and headed into the Tavern to work my first-ever dinner shift as a server.

As I sat in Rosie's, however, I had just come from the Mazda dealership to pick up my brand new 1997 Sahara Sand Protege, and was waiting to meet my friends for lunch. Paid personal days are a corporate perk I enjoyed.

It was late on a second summer afternoon during the lull between lunch and dinner service when I first walked into the Tavern to apply for a job. The 4 p.m. sun warmed my bare arms, making it feel like it was still August. Wearing a pair of cut-off jeans, a hugging, cream-colored tee, a smudge of blue eyeliner behind my lashes, and a sheath of self-assurance, my expectations were momentary. My hair was long with curly chestnut tresses, my skin still reflecting a caramel tint acquired at the Jersey Shore where I had honed some waitressing skills that summer. I was nineteen.

Following a quick but confident recitation of my restaurant resume, I asked the bartender, Big Bud, if they were hiring. With his back turned purposely toward me, he made a phone call upstairs to Phyllis, the general manager, briefly causing me to second-guess my indifference.

About a week later, Phyllis phoned and instructed me to show up Monday evening for training. Unbeknownst to me, server positions at the Tavern were coveted. I had nonchalantly walked into one of the most lucrative restaurants in Philadelphia seeking a waitress gig.

I remember being surprised when I learned the guy out front hosing down kitchen mats wasn't a janitor; he was the restaurant owner, Micky! If you knew South Philadelphians and the personal pride they took in the cleanliness of their homes, it wasn't such a stretch. Some of the women in my neighborhood wore their OCD cleaning regimens as a badge of honor; the more nuts you were, like cleaning light switches with Q-tips, the more authority you had to one up a neighbor.

Though I had grown up only ten blocks south of the Tavern, I never knew it existed before applying to work there. It certainly wasn't the red-checkered tablecloth Italian eateries where my family dined on special occasions. Tavern prices did not align with my parents' budget, especially when taking my three sisters and me out to dinner. Yet, from the minute I walked into the Tavern it felt familiar, like I was exactly where I was supposed to be. That was not often the case at that time of flux in my life.

Memories are confluences of acquired tactical and sensory experiences that exist outside of our present awareness and called upon as needed. At least that's the take-away I got from a Psych 101 course. Gazing at the Tavern, and occasionally at my new car parked in the lot, my recall of detail was precise, and my perspective on its meaning still sketchy.

While sitting and waiting for the girls to arrive for lunch

at Rosie's, I was preoccupied with a big relationship decision weighing on my mind. Plus, I was inside my head trying to reconcile the shifts I still maintained at the Tavern a few nights a week with my new promotion to vice president of marketing and communications at my day job at a commercial bank. Not to mention, I had to head back to the restaurant just a few hours after lunch to fill in as a bartender for Big Bud. *Dread!*

I had become loathsome of the physical work of carrying heavy trays up and down steps, salivating men who sat at the bar week after week, telling the same stupid jokes, and especially the counterculture morality that was the norm inside Tavern walls. So much so that I had begun fantasizing about being carjacked on my way to the restaurant, and would purposely drive through a rough neighborhood with my windows down to further tempt fate. *Sick. I know.* Yet, in my fantasy, I always got away unharmed. Personal days don't exist in the restaurant business, so a carjacking would be one of only a few legitimate excuses for missing a shift, especially on a weekend.

Sitting in the cafe, I had an uncomfortable cold feeling in my stomach sipping a glass of Philly "ice water." Although I knew I'd miss the extra two grand in cash I earned each month sidelining two nights a week at the restaurant, the environment had become painfully stagnant. My worlds were colliding.

Ivy was the first of my pals to arrive at Rosie's for lunch, breaking my silent consternation. After blowing a few air kisses to the familiar faces working behind the counter, she slid her wispy frame into the booth across from me and rested her designer-logoed shopping bags beside her.

"Look at that place, Valley Girl," she said, turning her attention to the Tavern through the window. Our waitress arrived seeking our beverage order.

"Perrier with a lime for me please," I requested.

"And I would just like a cup of hot water, please," Ivy ordered politely. Ivy always carried her own tea bags. I'm not sure whether this was a measure of frugality (*why pay for hot water?*) or to ensure she got precisely the type of tea she desired. She was a prudent money manager, but generous. Having dined with her enough times, I lovingly accepted Ivy's special orders. As a veteran waitress, one would think she knew better than to make requests that caused another server to take extra steps, like asking for skim milk for her coffee instead of cream. However, in exchange for Ivy's higher maintenance as the one being served, she was a good tipper to an indulgent server.

Though Ivy was closer in age to my mom, I regarded her more as a sister. Not only did she appear twenty years younger, but I believe our souls were aligned in a past life. We "got" each other implicitly.

"Who would believe the goings on in there, eh? You ought to write it down, I'm telling you. It would be a best seller."

"I wouldn't know where to start."

"Start with the Hoagie story," she suggested.

"You'd have to help me remember the details," I lied dismissively while pretending to read the menu I already knew by heart. "Besides, I think the *Frankie* story is a better start."

My words were met by Rachael's arrival. Rachael adorned a great smile and a contagious laugh—a high-end sales associate at the posh Baum's men's store uptown who chose her words carefully yet effortlessly. She was skilled in the ability to retort

4

to most comments with quick-witted, ambiguous comebacks, and easily managed her two concurrent demeanors. She was like dry ice: cool, yet subject to sublimation under precarious conditions. In the evenings, Rachael was one of the Tavern's veteran hostesses. Anyway, I guess the best way to illustrate her duality is to tell "the Frankie story."

Rachael and Frankie were in the middle of an ugly divorce. Frankie was a tow-truck driver by day and contented in the evenings with a TV remote control and an occasional hand job. He was in total denial of his inability to engage Rachael, a woman with loftier aspirations. She essentially married him to become part of his big and inviting family. She was an only child who grew up in a remote town near the Poconos.

Rachael remained unhappily married because of their eight-year-old son, Vito. But when Rachael lost interest in Frankie's short-sighted outlook, Frankie began accusing her of having an affair with Cap, the Tavern's night manager, among other abuses, which eventually led to their separation.

One night while Rachael worked the hostess stand, Frankie was playing his hand at verbal harassment via repeated phone calls to the restaurant. The phone rang and Rachael answered, "Hello, this is the Tavern. May I help you?"

"You whore!" he shouted into the receiver.

Click. She hung up the phone.

Turning to a pair of couples entering the restaurant, Rachael asked smiling, "Hello. How are you this evening? Table for four?" She escorted the well-dressed diners to a table by the window.

The phone rang again, and Rachael scurried back to the podium to answer it. Frankie shouted in Rachael's ear, "You ungrateful bitch! Don't think for one minute you'll get a

5

penny of my pension because I'm leaving it all to my sister."

Laughing out loud in mockery, Rachael responded, "Thank God I wasn't planning on retiring in a tent." She hung up on him again and stepped over to the bar to say hello to a few regulars having a drink.

Over at the hostess stand, the phone kept ringing. Rachael excused herself and quickly picked it up. She heard Frankie begin another name-calling streak. Whispering through clenched teeth, she warned him, "You better stop fucking calling me at work if you know what's good for you."

"Don't dare hang up on me, you dirty whore! Just wait until Vito is old enough to find out what his mother did…" Frankie's words hung in the air as if typed inside of a bubble on a cartoon strip. Rachael hung up on Frankie for the last time that night. Something had snapped. She turned to the coat check and said, "Greet the customers and ask them to wait at the bar. I'll be right back." The coat check girl stepped up without question, thinking maybe Rachael needed a reprieve. That was sort of true.

Rachael pushed through the swinging door and into the kitchen. She walked quickly and determinedly, first passing the hot line. She cut through the oily kitchen air like a chef's knife, deaf to clanging sauté pans. Jonesy, the kitchen expediter, watched without much significance as Rachael passed the garde-manger station en route to the side exit. She maintained a resolute gait and fixed focus as if she were on an urgent restaurant mission like heading outside to assist a customer with a valet issue.

But there were no customers waiting outside. No restaurant emergency.

Rachael crossed the little street to the municipal parking

lot, got into her tan sedan, slammed the door, and backed out of the parking lot onto 5th Street. She drove two blocks south and made a left turn onto Plumber Street where Frankie rented a house. She threw the car into park in the middle of the road, charged up the steps and rapped on the front door. Frankie opened it with a nasty smirk on his face, about to spew another insult at Rachael. But before he had time to articulate the "*f*" in *fuck*, Rachael took the black patent leather pump from her right foot and proceeded to beat him with its three-inch heel. Frankie's mere mention of their son on the phone was the cracking point for Rachael when reason could no longer be entertained.

"Don't you EVER, EVER harass me while I'm at work again!" she raged. "You son-of-a-bitch, tow-truck-driving jerk off! Do you understand?" She hammered her shoe heel into Frankie's shoulders as he attempted to block her thrusts with a forearm, backing his way into the house. Rachael was oblivious to the obnoxious melody of beeping horns from cars trapped behind hers on the street.

Fifteen minutes later, just as she had promised, Rachael was back at the hostess stand, menus in hand with a few mussed bangs. She greeted the next customers saying, "Right this way." There were no more calls from Frankie that night.

It was a story that we would retell repeatedly, nearly peeing ourselves laughing about the night that Rachael beat the shit out of Frankie and returned to seat customers without so much as smeared lipstick. Most things are funnier in hindsight.

Across from me at Rosie's, however, Rachael remained partially tuned in to the persuasion Ivy was dishing out to convince me to write a book about our shared experiences at the Tavern.

"Sounds good to me," Rachael approved with a "Why not?" shrug before looking away from our table to scope out who was yet to be seen at Rosie's.

Just then, Chrissy arrived, detained by a pet rescue emergency. She didn't weigh in about me writing a book or not but got right to the business of why we were there in the first place—eating. Chrissy was very slender and never had a weight problem, but she may have had a tapeworm. I don't think I'd ever seen a woman eat and enjoy food quite like she did. If my grandmother Josie was alive and sitting with us, she would have said, "God bless her," one of two possible Italian-inspired expressions for those with healthy appetites.

The other, which more likely would have come from my grandmother Mary's lips, was "*morte di fame*." Grandmom Mary, as we called her, pronounced it "*morta-dee-von*" in her bastardized Italian dialect. Literally translated: *dying from hunger*, a sarcasm and actual insult on the shores of Agropoli. Preparing, serving and eating food had protocols to which deviation was sacrilege in my upbringing. For Italians, most insults and derogatory words are centered on foods we love— *cetriolo*, pronounced in our neighborhood as "*jid-drool*" with a rolled "*r*," *finocchio*, pronounced, "*fin-oik*," and *melanzana* pronounced, "*moul-an-yan*." Go figure.

Anyhow, besides being a solid friend since pre-Tavern days, Chrissy practiced acupuncture and was the source of any knowledge I possessed about the esoteric meaning of yin/yang.

"Sorry I'm late," Chrissy apologized. "Whose lunch am I eating? Are these Jersey tomatoes? How are you feeling, Val?"

"I'm okay," I answered, even though I wasn't.

Ivy ignored Chrissy and circled back to the idea of a book.

"So, Val, what do you think? I think it would be fabulous. I'm telling you, this stuff would make a great movie. Who would play us in the movie?"

Rachael's wandering eyes spotted a familiar face entering the tiny cafe, triggering an ear-to-ear smile and exposing her magazine-white teeth. It was Louie, a Tavern regular. The Tavern had a way of breaking down barriers—age, social class, and education. We socialized with affluent regular customers in and outside of the restaurant. Regulars made up the persona of the place as much as the staff and had equally borne influence on my evolution.

"Well, look who's here," she announced. "Let's get the party started," and sprung up to greet Louie at the door as though she was hostessing the lunch shift.

Louie walked over to our table, leaning in to kiss me hello. "Who sent out the invites?" he asked, laughing. "I didn't get one. Hey Val, where's your other half?"

I smiled and shrugged.

"Are those two ever apart?" he smirked.

Louie always had the last two fingers of his right hand folded under slightly. I was curious as to whether this was due to an injury, or if maybe it was a mannerism he developed to make "greasing" more convenient as there was usually a Benjamin tucked under those fingers. Louie was the biggest spender I'd ever known and tipping servers was something he very well could have copyrighted.

We all chit-chatted, then Louie headed toward the back of Rosie's where he met with a few building contractors.

Rosie's cafe didn't exist when I started working at the Tavern. The building used to house the Tavern's off-premises bakery before Micky converted it into a bistro. Rosie's was somewhat misplaced in South Philly. Perhaps it should have been at the seashore with its ice cream parlor ambiance and Victorian tin ceiling. It was small and feminine, unlike the yang of its virile father, the Tavern, across the street. Rosie's bouncing chatter further distinguished it from the soft-spoken conversational murmurs eavesdropped by servers at the Tavern on any given night. Yet looking out Rosie's windows some afternoons were many of the same faces that looked back at it from the Tavern on a Saturday evening—regulars like Louie.

After my fill of the latest gossip, caprese salad and Sarcone's bread (arguably the best artisan bread in Philadelphia with its golden, sesame-seeded crust and airy center), I had to get home, change clothes, and head back to the Tavern to tend bar. As I walked toward my new car, I looked at the side entrance to the Tavern and retrieved my eleven-year tenure as if using the rewind feature on a remote control. My mind paused exactly where I began—in the outfit I had the audacity to wear to apply for a job, full of false bravado.

I scanned my memory in search of a thesis on the entire experience; the profound, fortune cookie one-liner that would summarize its overarching meaningfulness, to no avail. It was too experiential to encapsulate.

What I knew clearly, however, was that adeptness for turning a six-top in a timely fashion, or the ability to balance eight heavy plates on a serving tray on my shoulder without spilling an ounce of sauce had absolutely nothing to do with my hire. When I arrived at the Tavern as a college girl, I was about to embark on an education that would present experiences beyond any of those I had ever acquired in a classroom or learned growing up on Tasker Street.

I climbed into the front seat of my brand new Protege, shaking my head, thinking back on my naïveté when I began working there and how the place had transformed me over the years. Micky caught the corner of my eye. He was still outside hosing down the rubber kitchen mats on the sidewalk. So much had changed and yet nothing at all.

Corralled by the Tavern

When I began working at the Tavern, I hadn't been back home for a few years (*home* meaning South Philly) between attending college and spending summers at the Jersey Shore. My parents divorced during freshman year, selling our childhood home. My mom moved to Florida and my dad was living with my grandmother. So "home" for that moment in time was a studio apartment not far from the Tavern I shared with my British roommate-turned-boyfriend, Alex, an exchange student I met at school.

The city embraced me with familiarity with its aggregate sidewalk squares that served summer hopscotch players so well. A faded red, white and blue bicentennial sign was still affixed to the telephone pole at the corner of 8th and Mountain Street, and the dirt-encrusted subway rails and the rats that scurried along them still latticed the shady concourses beneath the skyscrapers. By the 80s, Philadelphia had suffered decades of being a dead blue-collar town. That was before a visionary mayor, the approaching millennium restaurant renaissance and a new sports complex brought it back to life. In its heyday, the Tavern had the distinction of being one of Philly's top restaurants, and *the* place to be seen by the city's most affluent. The Tavern was an inherently chauvinistic environment. It was conspicuous—to men, anyway.

As for me, a transfer junior at Temple University, waitressing would fund me for a couple of years until graduation so I could secure a "real" job in communications. If I had been a gambler like my dad, I would not have bet on working at the Tavern for just over a decade. In fact, I would have vehemently argued the point...and lost. This sentiment is shared by many of my Tavern cohorts who remained there well beyond their welcomes and way longer than the notoriously high turnover of most restaurant jobs. It would be easy to surmise it was the money that kept us there.

Either way, we all landed there on our way to someplace else. Someplace intriguing. Someplace with promise. Tavern women were well-educated and witty conversationalists. We were tall and petite, single, married, divorced, straight, bisexual, blonde, brunette, artists, teachers, ballerinas, lawyers, and doctors in the making. Our individuality made up a smorgasbord and offered an appeal for every appetite. We were also hard workers, enterprising, and skillful in the art of manipulation...whether that meant upselling a menu item or procuring an all-expenses-paid Caribbean vacation. Some of the most able and resourceful women I've known slung milk-fed veal across those artisan tile floors. Of course, none of these talents were criteria on the job application, but managers like Big Bud and Phyllis could sniff them out.

From the outside, the meticulous brick-faced Tavern offered rapport. Situated in a charming neighborhood of South Philadelphia in the heart of the city's oldest Italian American community, the Tavern was a block from Philly's artsy district and adjacent to one of its wealthiest neighborhoods. The excellent culinary options that now occupy Philly's uptown section had not yet arrived on the scene.

The Tavern was made up of what were once six row

houses that converged on the corner of a tiny street called Willow Street. It evolved over the years into a sexy, upscale dining establishment. Interestingly, I once served a woman who told me that she was born in the very spot where she sat eating her dinner that evening.

The inside told me a different story. First off, it wasn't a "tavern." In fact, the last time the place resembled any sort of a taproom was in 1969 when a skinny neighborhood guy (Micky) and his brother Sabby bought a corner bar and served roast beef sandwiches and ribs from a small kitchen in the back. It had quickly become a hangout for their friends and well-heeled contemporaries of their father, Mr. Marcello, a first-generation Italian American, Republican committeeman, founder of a local union, amateur boxer and Western movie aficionado. From the start, there was built-in character... and characters.

Winks to the senior Marcello would show up in subtleties such as an authentic Remington equestrian sketch in the dining nook behind the upstairs bar, and a framed photo of middleweight Hall-of-Famer and native South Philadelphian, Joey Giardello, which hung on an adjacent wall. Additionally, although the twentieth century was ending, liquor drinks were still served in coffee cups on election day—a tradition held over from Mr. Marcello's years as a politician and Philly's blue laws.

Micky and Sabby were the official Tavern owners. However, their older sister Rosie (the bistro's namesake) was silently involved and noticeably influential. Rosie was a nationally recognized illustrator, antiques connoisseur and quintessential elitist who I liked, nonetheless. She handpicked authentic pieces of the restaurant's decor like the brass, late-1800s working cash register, and the seventeenth century, wood-carved Native American statue that greeted customers at the door like the ones in old cigar shops.

Rosie was mannish. From behind she might have fooled you by her height, broad shoulders, and tailored pinstripe slacks suits. She smoked cigarillos. However, an about face revealed a high cheek-boned, oatmeal colored complexion offset by scarlet lipstick. Her looks were out of time and placed her on a World War II era movie set. In any case, she was responsible for selecting most of the restaurant's artwork.

A framed canvas adorned the wall behind the rich antique bar as you entered the restaurant. It was an oil painting of a woman wearing a low-cut blouse exposing the top half of her nipples. And, an interesting illustration hung on the wall inside the ladies' room. It was a 1930s cartoon rendering of seven young women holding up their aprons to expose their petticoats underneath. Sitting inside each of their cupped aprons, about groin height, was the head of a little pussy (cat, that is) peeking out.

The symbolic nature of these embellishments was lost, for a while, on the nineteen-year-old neighborhood girl who showed up casually on a late September afternoon with the objective of earning enough dough to cover textbooks and a car payment.

Each night before the dinner rush, Rosie would sit at the upstairs bar enjoying a glass of Tignanello, a robust Tuscan red wine, while pontificating about this philosophy or that to a few of us compulsorily polite staff members. While smiling and pretending to be in awe of her profoundness, I secretly thought she was benevolently narcissistic and full of shit at times, though she had me guessing.

I approached her one evening, kissing her on the cheek to greet her. She was happy to see me. I caught her mid-conversation with Pal Joey, the upstairs bartender.

"You see," she stated with authority, "women wear lipstick because what they're actually doing is painting their vaginas on their faces to attract men."

Hmm. I immediately conjured images of Japanese Kabuki makeup. As I said, she had me wondering.

What struck me about Rosie was her dichotomy. On the one hand, she seemed to want to be a man in order to counter or rebel against the dominant masculine subculture she inherited. On the other hand, she deliberately chose art and topics that would sexually subjectify women.

In any case, undoubtedly the most imposing artwork was a mural-sized nude painting hanging above the stairwell to the upstairs dining room whose brunette subject was rumored to have been the mistress of the late John ("Jack") B. Kelly Sr. (as in, Princess Grace's father). Lounging on a chaise, her cherubic figure greeted guests on their way up the rich stairwell to indulge in a porterhouse steak or a Stoli martini.

I speculated a lot about her over the years. At first, her unabashed appearance struck me. I figured if her man, Jack, was born in 1898, she could feasibly have been ten years his junior, placing her birth anywhere between the turn of the nineteenth century and the onset of the Roarin' 20s—the same overall time frame both my grandmothers, Mary and Josie, were born. Yet, I have difficulty picturing either of them posing nude. To the contrary, I am only able to visualize the two wearing house dresses and wielding frying pans and wooden spoons. Maybe a Pall Mall in hand.

I wondered what her name was. Ruby? Loretta? Maybe

just Anne. At times, folding napkins or polishing silverware in preparation for the evening shift, I felt like a gracious hand on duty in her mansion.

It seems I viewed her through an evolving set of lenses over my Tavern years. From each vantage point her significance transformed from naïve and smitten devotee, to flirt and scamp, to coveted concubine, to bitch, and finally, to a contented keeper of a wonderful secret. The latter I came to gravitate toward as the seasons passed and I found myself sharing her riddle.

Her face was regular. She wasn't stunning or mysterious. However, she had something that made her the worthy subject of a wall-sized portrait commissioned by her lover. Something sacred existed between the two of them, a "marriage" so compelling and erotic that only she and Jack needed to understand it.

Whatever their circumstances, "Anne" and the other works of art adorning the restaurant provided hunks of trivia for tableside chit-chat and added to the place's establishmentarianism. The suggestive art hanging on Tavern walls was hardly offensive to female patrons. Each piece was a small part of a larger, ornamental landscape appreciated by experts and admired by customers for their collective beauty. But they were by no means accidental.

Sabby, who passed away years before my hire, was said to have had a penchant for partying and a weakness for women. He was responsible for the all-female wait staff. And certainly, the women were the Tavern's most attractive feature; the lure that hooked regular male clientele week after week, or shift after shift, depending on your perspective.

Few of us were aware of this design—at least upon hire—

and certainly not me. The Tavern wasn't a gentleman's club, after all. It was as well known for healthy portions of the finest food as it was in some circles for the females who worked there. Of course, we were also clothed. House rules dictated dressing as though we were going out to dinner ourselves.

Still, if it were not for Micky's dedication and meticulous attention to detail, the restaurant would not have succeeded with or without the engaging staff and the persona of the place. They say that restaurant owners are married to their businesses, and in Micky's case, this is an entirely true statement. With Micky at the helm of the household, the rest of us made up the dysfunctional family members.

I say, if these three sibling entrepreneurs had sat down and mapped out their strategy in a boardroom as a formal business plan, both in subtleties and outward characteristics, they would have charted a brilliant case study for future marketing students.

So, wearing three-inch heels and for some, a bra a size too small, the nightly insanity ensued of delivering the finest Angus and epicurean dishes to a stream of potential fish to bait—the endless groups of men who frequented the restaurant because it was a legit place to fraternize with women Monday through Friday. Saturday was wife night.

The Hoagie Story

A s we prepared for the impending Saturday night rush to wait tables, laying tablecloths and preparing the dessert tray, Ivy inked on the back of a to-go lid what looked like a wide patch of grass. It was her memory of Hoagie's pubic area, and the vision that ended the relationship before it began.

She was in her early fifties, recently divorced and re-entering the dating scene. Hoagie came into the restaurant alone one night and left Ivy a $300 tip on an $85 check with an invitation to join him for an evening in New York City.

Of course, his personal limo would pick her up in Philly and escort her there. How bad could it be, she thought, to have a nice dinner in New York? In Ivy's full-time career, she was an art therapist for children. She was an intellectual and had a true interest in people. So, the fact that Hoagie was a little short in the looks department hadn't dissuaded her...yet.

Hoagie was built like a 1970s cartoon character with a square and boxy torso, stick-like legs, and wore a black, Hitler-type mustache. Hoagie, by the way, was a silly nickname we created based on his very long Turkish surname, and not because he resembled a famous Philadelphia sandwich. He did, however, bear an uncanny resemblance to Boris Badenov from *The Rocky and Bullwinkle Show*.

Anyway, everything went according to plan. The limo

arrived on time, the trip to New York was pleasant, and Hoagie entertained Ivy at one of the best restaurants in the city. Afterward, he invited her back to his upscale, two-story apartment on the Upper East Side for a nightcap. A little out of kilter from all the alcohol consumed, Hoagie excused himself to change his clothes. When he re-entered the library from a stairwell across the room where Ivy sat sipping an exquisite bourbon in a snifter, he was wearing button-down, pinstripe pajamas. That was his first mistake.

As he awkwardly made his way down the steps, his pajama bottoms fell to his ankles, exposing a wall-to-wall carpet of pubic hair that extended from his left hip to his right, as Ivy illustrated for the growing number of Tavern servers and busboys looking over her shoulders at her sketch. Back in N.Y., "Like any good mother would," according to Ivy, she helped him back into his pj's before politely exiting the posh apartment.

In side-splitting laughter, we began the weekly insanity of serving sports celebs, funeral directors, doctors, contractors, news anchors, politicians, mobsters, actors performing in town and the endless groups of businessmen who frequented the restaurant.

But, Saturday nights were reserved for wives. So the charming, predominantly female Tavern servers offered lighter fare to the consorts while chatting up the hottest designer trends. Whether or not some of us were conscious about our behavior is subject to argument, but it was nonetheless a two-fold strategy: rapport with the wives allayed suspicions they may have had about their husbands' frequent visits to the restaurant, keeping the rest of the week's predominantly male business and outrageous tips flowing. It also built trust among our regulars. We were cool.

I remember serving two women one Saturday evening. One was in her early seventies and the other in her late fifties. The elder woman asked me if knew a customer named Sal Rosella. I innocently responded, "Oh, yes. Mr. Rosella and his lovely wife are here almost every Thursday night. She looks like a model. They're so nice."

To that the woman's entire demeanor changed, and she pointed her finger at me and said, "That whore's not his wife. I'm embarrassed to say he's my son, and *this* is his wife!" pointing to the other woman at the table.

I nearly died on the spot. Of course, I apologized profusely and explained I had no idea before running to confess to our manager, Cap (short for "Captain" and borne of his signature drink, a Captain Morgan and Diet Coke with a lime wedge. Like many other ingenious South Philly nicknames, Cap was a double entendre because he was the "captain" of the restaurant at night and ran the show).

Cap took me by the shoulders and warned, "Let this be a lesson to you. NEVER give information about a customer to another customer. I'm going to let this slide because you didn't know any better. But, now you do. Mr. Rosella is one of our best Thursday night regulars and he's very influential with the cardinal and the dioceses."

Pure irony.

Back in the storage room, with the sketch of Hoagie's pubes, Ivy embarked on an unplanned succession of dating escapades. Better yet, comic relief between adrenaline-filled trips up and down the kitchen stairs during Saturday dinner rushes as Ivy kept us updated with her saga of midlife crotch encounters.

There was Rising Robert, the attorney with a penile implant that gave him bravado to model his unit from beneath his Speedo-style undies, all while bragging about his ability to stay erect for hours. "Sure! Who couldn't, with bionics?" Ivy used to say. Above and beyond, she reported, the wiring mechanism in his balls made them feel like they were filled with Christmas tree lights.

Continuous Ken had a problem reaching orgasm. Many a night I yelled down to Ivy over a tray of steaming mussels as I climbed the kitchen steps, "Anything yet?" And she'd shake her head no. I often imagined the eventual pressure release catapulting Ivy through the drywall. Fortunately, it never happened.

Poor Resting Richard took Prozac for depression. He warned Ivy before their first kiss that there was a ten percent chance he'd be impotent.

And, of course, there was Limp Larry, who needed a little help getting up...from his chair. By the time Limp Larry came into the picture, Ivy had just about had it with dating. She said that if she had met a one-eyed Eskimo midget who was functional in the penis department, she would consider him. Of course, this all predated the advent of Viagra, and political correctness.

But my personal favorite was Goodness-God-Great-Balls-of-Fire-and-Brimstone George who took the names of the Holy Trinity and saints in vain as he reached orgasm. "Jesus, Mary and Joseph! Mother of God! Jesus Christ Almighty!" he shouted in ecstasy. With Ivy being Jewish, the irony was not lost on her.

Amid the dysfunction, the Tavern girls reeled in some live ones and treated us all to the envy-worthy hot details. Along with all the other not-ready-for-prime-time moments, these made our experience at the restaurant bearable, memorable and unfathomable.

Guiltless and Panty-Free

There were some wildly adventurous girls at the Tavern with stories that awed me. I did a lot of listening in the storage room where we sat waiting for our tables to be seated but kept my own sex life relegated to my bedroom. After all, back then my stories were boring, comparatively. I mean, I had never slept with nor even made out with a celebrity or a famous athlete. Moreover, my boyfriend Alex wasn't that interested in sex…with me, anyway. For some reason it took me years before I questioned his preference. Something between making as little contact with my breasts as possible, and fighting me over kitchen curtains eventually would have me thinking.

So, when Dana talked about riding TV's hottest cop during a taxi drive through New York City, I thought to myself naïvely, *Wow! How did she penetrate those privileged circles?*

Dana mingled with more celebrities than anyone I knew then or know now. How did she attract them? I'm not talking from a looks perspective. She was athletic and cute in a country club way with a little turned up nose, bouncy blonde hair and a great body. But many of the Tavern women were uniquely beautiful. Yet, Dana was a fame magnet. I'm talking about hanging out with the likes of Smokey Robinson, Tug McGraw and Rod Stewart. She even met and socialized with Bill Clinton once at a political function. Thinking back, she didn't have hang-ups or guilt trips about promiscuity. She was not the least bit intimidated, and she was very inviting. Most of all, she was fun.

Dana was completely carefree. One night we were in the makeshift dressing room on the restaurant's third floor and she was rustling through a box of lost and found items. She was looking for a pair of pantyhose to wear because she had forgotten hers. No doubt, any pantyhose left in the dressing room had already put in a shift or two. But that didn't dissuade Dana. She pulled a pair of wrinkled black hose from the cardboard box, returned them to the right-side-in, and slipped them onto her panty-less lower half.

On another night, Dana was at the bathroom mirror applying lip gloss and murmured, "Hmmm. I can still smell Ginger on my clothes," to Rachael and me.

Rachael asked, "Oh, were you baking today?"

Laughing through her fingers, Dana snorted, "God, no! Ginger is Marty's show horse. I came here directly from the stables today." She did not fret in the least that she was about to serve lobster tails smelling like liniment, hay, or worse under her saddle. Nothing bothered this girl. She was the diametric antithesis of me in almost every possible way.

I was fortunate not to be born an envious person of material items or someone else's success despite the sense of lack that framed my childhood. But, I *was* a little jealous of people who operated free of guilt and obligation or second-guessing decisions. These were anchors that held me back as a young girl from realizing limitless possibilities. The Tavern presented a Pandora's box of options…but all came with conditions. *Conditions* did not threaten Dana.

Marty, Ginger the horse's owner, was an equestrian

enthusiast and chairman of the Devon Horse Show Foundation. A mainline Philadelphia suburb, Devon is home to the oldest and largest outdoor multi-breed horse show in the United States. I thought to myself, *Now how in the hell did Dana get that job? Did she sleep with Marty, too?* I don't believe the man measured more than 5'4" tall and had a terrible comb over. Nice guy, but definitely unattractive. Nonetheless, Marty was one of the blue bloods with loads of old Philly money.

Speaking of blue bloods, Dana's unbridled nature was the source of another Tavern classic...

It was a Saturday night and the Whites arrived for an early dinner ahead of the usual weekend crowds just as the doors opened. Aside from staff, the restaurant was empty. Rachael escorted them from the bar to Table 1 downstairs, their favorite spot.

A dark, beveled wood wall partitioned the two downstairs dining rooms. At the far end of the wall was a cut out window embellished with decorative wrought bars across the opening, allowing one to see into the adjacent room. John Travolta Jerry, the place's only male waiter, who was as bright as could be and killing time at the Tavern before deciding on a "real" career, and clearly resembled John Travolta, greeted the Whites. They were a late sixties country club couple. Their table was situated in front of the window opening in the partition wall, but they were seated with their backs to it.

"Good evening. Would you like to hear tonight's specials?" Jerry asked.

"Of course!" Mr. White obliged. Mrs. White tried to steady the room with one squinty eye over her martini glass.

Jerry began, "This evening's soup is a Tuscan white bean with bits of baby carrots..." Just then, Dana caught his eye.

She had appeared in the window behind the Whites.

She had casually walked through the empty dining room on the opposite side of the partition wall, as if to inspect table settings (something that would never occur to her to do in her role as a server). She paused at the window facing John Travolta Jerry, with the Whites' backs toward her. As soon as Jerry looked up and noticed Dana standing there, she quickly lifted her sweater and did a little dance, giving her bare nipples a good bounce, then gave Jerry a wink and nonchalantly moved on to inspect other nearby tables. Jerry stuttered the description of the soup and cleared his throat to choke back a guffaw.

We didn't know how he managed to keep his composure (and that was before Dana's boob job). He ended his monologue a few entrees short and rushed back to the kitchen where we all sat laughing our asses off. The Whites had no inkling of what transpired behind their backs. They were already three Gibsons in when they were seated at the table to begin with—not to mention being totally removed from each other or the world around them.

I came to observe over years at the Tavern that the country clubbers were the weakest tippers and least likely to part with cash. They were a frugal bunch, for the most part. My grandmother Josie always said, "A fool and his money are easily parted." These customers were great to know when in need of a job or a school referral, but mostly everyone else was regarded as servant status. We were tolerated when slumming to South Philly for sport and perhaps a good adventure story to share at the next cribbage night. Dana knew how to work them for at least an eighteen percent tip. A thoroughbred herself, she was a virtuoso at working all of our regulars.

I was different, and a little naïve, too. The savvy women hired by the Tavern quickly learned the fast track to success and the greatest skill one could hone there: manipulation. This was at the heart of my "problem." I had minimal training in the art of manipulation. To the contrary, I was well schooled at being manipulated. At my core, I am a giver, not a taker and have to exhaust all possibilities about someone's behavior before accepting shadowy truths about them. And then I'm done.

Even so, I couldn't understand why our wealthier or more famous customers invited some of the other girls to parties, on trips, wined and dined them, or requested them over the rest of us, and, aside from the country club set, left outrageous tips.

These girls were certainly good looking, but silently I considered some of them phonies or gold diggers and wondered why others couldn't see through their superficiality. They were in a clique and could tell private jokes about events they attended with high rollers. *Pick me*, I silently wished. *I am real, for crying out loud…and fun, and sexy, and smart, too!*

What I eventually figured out was that some of our well-heeled, high-profile regulars were not looking to fall in love or for a "real" relationship. They wanted to win a trophy. Moreover, there was the appeal of the conquest without emotional strings, something superficial women communicated without words. A mutually beneficial arrangement of givers and takers I'd come to watch play out time and time again.

Once again, my grandmother's words would come to mind. This time, Mary's; she always told me that it was just as easy to hook a rich man as it was a poor one. *Hmm. She lived most of her life inches above the poverty line…and I stink at fishing.*

Nevertheless, I believed even the girls like Dana, who successfully lured big spenders, deep down wanted the men to want them for something more than sex and a showpiece. They wanted the fairy-tale ending, too.

Watching the money game play out at the Tavern was edifying and intimidating. It was shocking at first. I began to believe a pattern: *for people who have loads of disposable money, spending it must be easy*—a revelation so unfamiliar to me from my humble upbringing. The loaded Tavern men would teach me that it is far easier to dole out money to buy status, companionship and "friends" than it is to provide intangibles like vulnerability, honor, advocacy or commitment. It's also the best ever, hand-is-quicker-than-the-eye distraction from reality.

Tippy, a gorgeous, half-African American, half-French, well-spoken young woman from Michigan and part-time hostess could have gotten anything she wanted from her lover, Peter, a Pennsylvania Supreme Court justice. Tippy found herself frequently threatening to go to Peter's wife and "out" their relationship…unless he paid for her and her friends to vacation in the Virgin Islands, set her up in her own business, or funded her condo on Rittenhouse Square. It worked well. She knew it was an idle threat that, if followed through, would not behoove her lifestyle. Still, Peter never had the cajones to call her bluff and bought into the threat every time. Well, in fairness, his conformity wasn't always a total layup for Tippy. He once tried explaining his concern to her that if any possible scandal would make its way to his appointer, the governor, it would be the end of his career. She aptly told Peter that in such a case, he should consider asking the governor for all future blowjobs.

Fueling the exchange between these pairs seemed to be a "loyalty among thieves" mentality that existed in the Tavern's nonconforming atmosphere. Things that took place inside the restaurant remained there (until now, anyway). So, many of the Tavern women were not only attractive and fun to be around, they were also cool. Wealthy, married men could especially enjoy the sanctity of our company.

I once tagged along with Dana to a Billy Joel concert in hopes that I could rub elbows with band members in her discard pile. Actually, my hope was that I would be recognized as a hidden gem and get inducted into the elite club to which she seemed to belong. Of course I would meet the one celebrity looking for a genuine relationship with a "real" girl with whom to fall in love. That did not happen. But, I guess attending this concert is what eventually led to my premier brush with fame. Well, it was more like a waft.

The Phantom B.J.

The Tavern was the first environment where I'd ever been exposed to such graphic sexual discussions and openness. It took some getting used to. You'd think after four years attending an all-girls, boy-crazed Catholic high school, followed by a few years of living in a co-ed college dorm, that I would have heard everything and anything from my peers by then.

Growing up in my neighborhood, it was actually more virtuous to have intercourse with your boyfriend than to have oral sex. Oral sex was supposed to be out of the question for cleanly Italian girls. Put it this way: if it went on, nice girls never admitted to it. "B.J.s" were for "Jersey girls" and "skanks." The rumor about Jersey girls using oral sex to avoid losing virginity was likely started by one boy spilling the tea boastfully to his South Philly friends about a date with a girl who lived on the other side of the Walt Whitman bridge, where people from our neighborhood who "made it" moved. True or not, when the boys bragged this way, it made some of the local girls jealous of their wins and provided a license to create a derogatory stereotype. In hindsight, I wonder who protected their virtue better—us or them.

Francesca seemed to bridge that gap at the Tavern, at least where blowjobs were concerned. A tall, lean woman with a lovely mop of bright red-from-a-bottle flowing curls that reached the small of her spine, she was originally from a neighborhood like mine. Francesca had spent several years in the early 80s living in alternative Center City neighborhoods when many closet doors remained closed, so her posse of male gay friends added to the artsy persona she wished to portray. It set her apart from the girls I knew growing up.

An aspiring actress, Francesca, or "Reds" as Jonesy called her, provided great instruction one night on pretending how to "swallow" as we stood watching beneath a shelf of meticulous rows of extra virgin olive oil. Francesca had this trick down to a science and we all paid close attention to the method. "It's an illusion," she said. "The trick is how you position your mouth." She proceeded to illustrate using a half loaf of seeded Sarcone's Italian bread as a makeshift penis (clearly the prosthesis had greater girth than any real, human penis, but sufficed), and some liquid hand soap. It was a demonstration that had even the busboys captivated. There had to be no less than nine staff members gathered around Francesca's improv.

Ivy happened to be passing the storage room en route to deliver a tray of veal Milanese to guests in the dining room. She rested the tray on the counter to catch a few minutes of the seminar. "God knows, I could use a few pointers," she said.

Elise, one of the other girls listening in, said dismissively, "That's too much work. I just swallow."

Francesca reverted to her South Philly roots and mimicked a dry heave. "Ew, disgusting!" she screeched. "It tastes like bleach."

And I, a typical Italian girl, couldn't help but think what a sin it was to waste a good loaf of Sarcone's bread.

One of Fran's audience members was Stephie from St. Louis who had the face of a porcelain doll with beautiful, flawless ivory skin, perfectly outlined crimson lips, and a unique sense of style. She was excellent at camouflage clothing and offered the other girls helpful tips on accessorizing. She was on her way to L.A. to study makeup artistry at a prestigious school.

As Ivy returned from serving the veal entrees, Stephie pulled her into the storage room. "Got a minute?" she asked, looking around to ensure they were alone. "I need your advice on something," Steph continued in the same tone I'd use to ask a friend for a stock tip. "Do you think $100 is an appropriate amount to charge for the type of service Francesca described?" she inquired, winking at Ivy.

Ivy, a little bewildered, countered, "Are we talking about what I think we're talking about?"

"Well, let's just say when a certain local gangster comes for lunch on Fridays, I disappear to the coatroom for a while," Steph divulged proudly.

With many years of therapy under her belt, Ivy answered with a question, "Steph, do you really think the money is worth it?"

To which Stephie replied after thinking for a moment, "Hmmm. Well, he has a small penis and finishes quickly."

At that, Ivy agreed that $100 was sufficient. What else could she say to Stephie's logic? Besides, the thought of recommending the "Francesca Method" would have taken far too long for a lunch shift, and Steph did have other tables to tend.

I'd love to know how this deal was struck initially. *Did it start as a tongue in cheek request from the guy? Was she desperately in need of the money, or maybe craved the attention? Was Stephie a thrill seeker and did she like the risk of possibly getting caught on her knees in the coatroom? Was she attracted to him?* I mean, he was a powerful, handsome and distinguished-looking man with striking blue eyes.

This story occupied space in my head in a disturbing way. I questioned whether I was just not a free love kind of person or if behind Stephie's flawless face lurked a sadly low self-image. I wondered why she didn't seem concerned about the reputation she was carving for herself. I realized these questions were formulated from my point of view and that at least one other perspective existed for Stephie. Then again, it *was* the Tavern where boundaries were safely blurred.

ANOTHER PHANTOM B.J.

When I was a skinny twelve-year-old girl running through the streets of my neighborhood with no less than fifteen other kids playing jailbreak on a summer night, I was happy as a clam to be sporting a pair of hand-me-down, mustard yellow, low-top Chuck Taylors. It didn't matter to me that the sneakers were gently worn by my older cousin because they were a name brand, something very underrepresented in my modest wardrobe in 1977. Besides that, they matched my Rocky-inspired jogging shorts and tank top perfectly.

My sisters and I generally got new things once or twice a year either by necessity or at Christmas. Otherwise, I had female cousins between one and four years older, so I was the recipient of trash bags full of hand-me-down clothing. Most of the items were too big for me, but I was happy to have them. I couldn't wait to rustle through a sack handed over during a family visit to see what outfits I could put together.

Circa those years, I never owned a KISS or a Deep Purple T-shirt. I never owned a Phillies, Eagles or Flyers sweatshirt. Likewise, I never hung posters of my favorite musicians or actors or *Teen Beat* covers on my bedroom walls. This was more the result of a lack of spending money than it was of interest. So, when my next-door neighbor gave me Billy Joel's *The Stranger* album for my thirteenth birthday, I not only treasured it, I memorized it. Every word to every song. The forward and the back cover copy, every band member, and any associated trivia I could get my hands on such as the inspiration provided by Billy's drummer, Liberty DeVitto on "Only the Good Die Young" and the fact that Billy wrote that song while opening for The Beach Boys in Knoxville, Tennessee. These kinds of tidbits were considered cool especially when talking to boys.

Later, in the 80s when I had my own money from working, my best friends growing up, August, Elaina, Ralphie, Jimmy and I got to go to his concerts, and Philly was always on the roster. He loved playing here! We knew the words to every song, which wasn't saying too much because most people knew the words to Billy Joel songs. They were easy sing-alongs, and his hits were overplayed on the radio. What differentiated me as a super fan, though, was my interest and knowledge of the less popular songs. I knew recording histories, composers, writers, vocalists and more.

There was one song that debuted in the early 90s, which was not popularized on the radio: "Code of Silence." The harmonica open was haunting and the background and chorus vocalizations by Cyndi Lauper were stirring. The lyrics eerily reminded me of a tragic story of a young girl from my neighborhood whom I had heard was the victim of incest. The song made me cry when I thought of this little girl. I was certain "Code of Silence" was written about a similar story. I shared my interpretations with my outside-of-the-Tavern posse, Elaina, August, Jimmy and Ralphie, as well as with the Tavern gals when we'd kill time in the restaurant storage room waiting for our tables to be seated (the latter of whom I didn't think paid any mind to what I was saying during bouts of dinner lulls and idle chit-chat). Surprisingly, no one else seemed to know this song.

Meanwhile, the Tavern had become Billy Joel's favorite Philadelphia restaurant. He was in good company as the restaurant had been frequented by many famous people over the years—Grace Kelly, Bruno Kirby, Pamela Anderson, George Peppard, Charles Barkley, Dr. J, Joe Frazier, Allen Iverson, Bette Midler, Joe Torre…to name just a few.

One Friday night my older sister asked me to babysit. I had to jump through a few hoops in order to convince someone to take my shift that night so I could accommodate my sister. It was summertime and business was threatening to be slow by the lack of reservations on the books, otherwise there would have been no chance of taking off a weekend night. Finally, John Travolta Jerry agreed to work for me so I, in turn, agreed to babysit for my sister.

I nearly died when I heard that Billy Joel and Christie Brinkley had dinner at the Tavern that night. Worse, John Travolta Jerry waited on them in what would have been *my* station! At the urging of the other customers, Billy Joel himself asked the Tavern pianist if he could borrow the keys for a little while. He had the entire restaurant on its feet.

By the following Monday night when I returned to work, Jerry was still glowing with excitement as he relayed the story of Billy Joel's performance to those of us who hadn't worked that Friday, as well as to our Monday night regulars. Even the local news made mention of the spontaneous event. Oh, did I mention that my sister canceled her plans at the last minute that Friday, and I sat at home watching TV instead of waiting on Billy Joel?

The following year, I temporarily left bank marketing for

a short stint at a newly launched ad agency and had some scheduling flexibility. So, I picked up an easy lunchtime hostess shift at the Tavern. When I arrived for work one morning, Phyllis called me upstairs to the office. *Uh oh,* I thought, *did I not accessorize appropriately Saturday night, or did I forget to charge somebody for a bottle of wine?*

To my shock, she informed me that Billy Joel and his manager were coming in for lunch. She instructed me where to seat them, and a few other special orders. From that moment onward, Phyllis's speech became mutated in my ears, like that of the teachers in the Charlie Brown cartoons.

I returned to the dining room and waited by the restaurant's entrance the entire lunch shift to ensure I'd be the first to greet Billy upon his arrival. This meant slacking on my other duties. But Little Miss Virgo cared less about following the rules that day. I was out of my mind and completely obsessed with what I would say when I greeted Billy.

As other regulars arrived for lunch, I'd say without making eye contact, "Sit anywhere today except the round table by the window. That one's reserved." ...Even to my pal Louie when he walked in.

He said, "Ay. What's a matta with you?"

I whispered in his ear that Billy Joel was expected any minute. He just laughed. He understood. I handed him and his friends a few menus and told them to seat themselves.

I couldn't let this opportunity pass. I'd have only a few minutes to be intriguing, charming, funny and coy as I walked Billy to his table, told him the specials and got him a drink. We would laugh and he would take a genuine interest in our conversation and ask me questions about myself when I'd visit his table throughout the meal.

Billy Joel evaded me that day. Again. And despite the clear lack in service I provided, Louie still inconspicuously handed me the usual folded C-note as he left the restaurant, which, by the way, was the easiest money I ever made. I could always count on my friend, Louie. Rest his generous soul.

A year later, Billy Joel was back in Philly on a concert tour. I arrived at work excited and announced to the girls during our daily "specials" meeting—our usual nightly pre-dinner meeting where Cap would present us with the extensive list of special, seasonal delights not included on the regular menu—that I had dibs on Billy Joel or anyone from his entourage should they show up at the Tavern that night. All had agreed. They knew the history and my level of fandom. Besides, they had their own Tavern fish to catch.

What I didn't realize was that Dana was scheduled to be the food runner that evening. *Drats!* A potential snag in the plan. The good news was that food runners only worked a few hours during the dinner rush to help deliver hot food to tables in the event that a server could not make it to the kitchen in time. Perhaps a waitress was tending to another table or opening a bottle of wine, or she was somewhere she wasn't supposed to be, like in the coatroom. In any case, I was hoping that none of this would be cause for Dana to leave the kitchen. After all, it was a Monday night and generally lower key than weekends.

I continued waiting on my tables on standby for someone from Billy's group to show. I had a strong intuition they would. Suddenly, Dana ran upstairs to the storage room and announced that she had just secured three front-row seats and backstage passes to the Billy Joel concert from a sound technician at a table downstairs. For Christ's sake, she only appeared at his table for two minutes to serve a freaking order of Clams alla Lanza and a Caesar salad! This is exactly what I meant about Dana. There was something in that girl's DNA—a scent that could be immediately detected by celebrities, athletes, mega stars, and moguls.

I begged and pleaded with her to take me along with one of the other tickets, but she had already promised them to her sister and her best friend Darla, a former Tavern server. As a consolation, she agreed that if I could get my own concert tickets, she would meet me on the concourse at the old behemoth Veterans Stadium during intermission and hand off the backstage passes so I could take a turn.

I was in!

There was not a single doubt in my obsessed mind that I would hook up with Billy Joel that night, be invited to an after-concert party and begin dating him. He and Christie were officially broken up by then and rumor had it he was single. Billy was from New York. In addition to being creative writers, we had that East Coast, city colloquial familiarity going for us, too. We would eventually collaborate on a monster hit, vacation in the Hamptons, and travel the world together. I would naturally quit the Tavern and be remembered during tableside conversations as the quintessential Cinderella story by the girls I left behind.

As the weekend approached, I worked out extra hard, tanned and had my nails done. I looked pretty cute wearing a snug, short-sleeved, periwinkle cotton tee that accentuated my tan, not to mention my best Tavern assets, and a pair of jean shorts and ankle cowgirl boots. I looked as fun-loving as Dana, but if she was an all-American girl, I was an all-Italian American one. Night and day. That was a good thing for the same reason there are ass men and breast men. A lid for every pot, as I was told.

I was able to score tickets to the concert from Louie, albeit they were in the super suites at Vets Stadium. The suites were okay for watching a football game in the dead of winter—if you had binoculars. You could keep warm, socialize, have a few drinks and catch what you missed on the closed-circuit TVs. But for watching a concert, you might as well have been at home watching it from your sofa. Hey, beggars can't be choosers (the sayings just keep on coming), and August and Elaina were thrilled to go.

Thanks to Louie, the tickets got me there. Then I had to execute the intermission plan to secure the backstage passes from Dana.

No sooner did the lights dim that I was at the elevator ready to meet Dana on the concourse and claim the pass to my future. Little did I know that to prevent ticket fraud, stadium management had instituted a new policy restricting patrons from leaving the suites. The guard at the elevator was unbending. I was completely deflated. I mean, I literally sank to the floor nearly tripping bathroom goers over my protruding buck suede boot tips.

Elaina and August had never before seen their practical friend behave this way. They scolded me to get up. With no other option, the three of us returned to the suite to watch the remainder of the concert on the closed-circuit TV. When the performance resumed after intermission, the cameras panned the front row of audience members. Right there before my teary eyes were Dana and Darla swaying to the music and holding Billy's outstretched hands as he bent over the crowd before him. Well, if that wasn't salt on a wound, as my mom would say.

I returned to the Tavern the next day and everyone got a chuckle from the story. Later that week a bunch of us Tavern girls met for coffee at Francesca's house. Dana recounted her night with Billy's guitarist through a mouthful of chewed bagel and cream cheese. As her buzz waned in the wee hours of the night after the concert, she realized she was completely turned off, even through the filter of alcohol. After all, he was a second stringer. The aha moment came in the hotel bed. So, she rolled over and said, "Dude, do what you want on my back. I got to get some sleep." We laughed so hard some of us spit out Francesca's delicious chicory coffee.

MOTHERFUCKERS

It promised to be another tremendously busy Saturday night, which meant we would each turn our tables between three and five times. The beautiful, hand-carved bar upstairs was dimly lit with antique sconces and packed six-deep with couture customers, waiting their turns for a table. Hard to imagine that people were actually willing to wait up to two hours at times to have dinner at the Tavern, which in and of itself created enormous pressure on the staff. Technically, we couldn't rush customers once they were seated. Not at Tavern prices.

Adding to the evening's stress was the infamous list of specials that had to be recited at each table. I think I once counted forty-two items. There were no cheat sheets allowed at the Tavern. We servers were expected to know each item and every ingredient in it, from the ranch where the cattle came that provided the porterhouse steak to the sea where the fish swam before swimming in an au jus en papillote. Believe me, we were no commodity, so making a mistake was a scary proposition. There were always at least five to ten women, including co-workers, waiting to take your shifts. The Tavern was among the most lucrative restaurants in Philadelphia to work and for that privilege we had to suffer certain humiliations.

As if balancing a 40 lb. tray on your right shoulder and a

"jack" in your left hand to place it on, contorting through a standing-room-only crowd in a pair of heels while a beeper on your waist incessantly summoned you back downstairs to the kitchen to pick up the next table's appetizers, and a hostess pressured to seat long-waiting customers hounded you to turn a table more quickly wasn't stressful enough, our male co-workers in the kitchen made sure to amp things up. Basically, they resented our ability to reap enormous tips among other opportunities as frontline employees when they were quite literally behind the lines cooking the celebrated menu items. These guys especially felt we needed to be kept in check.

One such humiliation was the random snarling treatment by the chief expediter in the kitchen, Jonesy. Jonesy's timing and command in the kitchen was excellent; not too many restaurant kitchens could churn out consistently high-quality, perfectly cooked, piping hot meals in such volume as did the Tavern cooks under Jonesy's watch, meeting the standards of restaurant snobs from near and far.

But like the rest of us, Jonesy had his faults. He was a bad gambler when he wasn't orchestrating six line cooks and two cold prep guys in the preparation and delivery of 300 dinner checks on a Saturday night.

When Jonesy had a bad week, God help the girl who broke his balls, which didn't take much effort. Actually, the restaurant environment presented a *safe* outlet for his personal anger issues. Except for the one time when he got a Mediterranean salad thrown in his face by a least likely source. It was soft-spoken Marina, a prima ballerina, who launched the cold appetizer at Jonesy. He had figured her all wrong when he barked, "Pick up your fuckin' food, you skinny bitch." She, today, is remembered in Tavern annals for *her* balls and the girl who got away with it unscathed, even by management.

Anyway, it never took long to realize when Jonesy was in a bad way. On those nights, rationale was absent. It didn't matter if a fantastic regular customer requested a special order, or if Jonesy's own mother did. The unfortunate waitress who had the task of presenting that order to him was in for it. It was like Oliver Twist asking for more soup.

At one time or another, we were all subject to his wrath. A quick-witted woman named Cheryl who hailed from Philly's Kensington section always joked she thought her middle name was "Motherfucker" after her first year at the Tavern. "Correct that," she'd say, "Irish Motherfucker." Only there could this treatment be tolerated (*and I reluctantly use the word*). And, in a bizarre way, it was somehow appropriate. If you knew Jonesy back then, or management for that matter, "Motherfucker" was not a curse. It was a commonly accepted proper noun.

Even Jonesy's "affectionate" names for some girls would be cause for a lawsuit in any other setting. He called Chrissy, who smoked a lot, "Phillip Morris," and Melanie, "Slop Bucket" though I'm not sure why. His alternate term for Cheryl when he was in a good mood was "Mayonnaise Face." It went more like this: "Pick up your fucking food while it's hot, Mayonnaise Face." Yet, no one seemed to mind. Money has the power to invoke blindness and deafness at times, even for the least likely of us.

But getting back to special orders, one punishment for this offense on a bad Jonesy night included holding up your entrees while you squirmed to diffuse angry, drinking and hungry customers with creative and reasonable explanations as to why their food was taking so long. And it was important to do everything possible to impart to the hostess, desperate to turn tables, that it wasn't your fault…or else you would have to face her wrath. Unlike Jonesy's verbal abuse, if you crossed the hostess, you jeopardized your earn-ability. She was the dining room power broker who controlled the seating.

Speaking of special orders… I had the privilege of serving the Finkels and the Goldentsteins one night. I have an active mind, the kind that needs to do a crossword puzzle during TV commercials while watching a movie. As such, I would create new challenges for myself at the restaurant to justify the mundane and physically laborious aspects of being a server. Of all nights, I chose this one to begin taking orders without writing them down. I started with a deuce—a table for two in restaurant language. By the time the Finkels and the Goldentsteins were seated, I had increased my challenge to a table of four.

Without thinking, I approached them with excitement like I had arrived at a bar on quiz night. *Weird Virgo girl.* Now these were no ordinary patrons. They were certified MFers in special ordering. I believe torturing restaurant servers was their personal form of entertainment.

No sooner had I arrived at their tableside did the women begin shouting beverage orders at me simultaneously:

"I'll take a Maker's Mark Manhattan on the rocks. Just a little ice. With a cherry. Make sure it's Maker's Mark and not a cheaper brand. On second thought, no ice—just chill it, serve it up, and bring the ice on the side," Mrs. Finkel yelled over her husband's cross-table conversation with Mr. Goldenstein about the Eagles' quarterback, Randall Cunningham's sixty-yard pass for a ninety-five-yard touchdown against Buffalo the week before.

Overlapping orders by Mrs. Goldenstein:

"I want an Absolut martini, up, very dry. With an olive. Make it two olives. Rocks on the side. Make sure it's Absolut. And make sure it's ice cold but not watered down."

"Wait. Shouldn't you be writing this down?" asked Mrs. Finkel.

"I'm trying to create new challenges for myself," I said smiling. As the words came out of my mouth, I knew instantaneously I had sealed my own fate. My admission was all the incentive these two needed to put me to the test. It was game on. As I walked away from their table to the bar to place the detailed drink order, I heard Mrs. Finkel yell from behind, "Make it three cubes of ice and the rest on the side."

When someone begins their experience at a restaurant special ordering the ice cubes in their drink, every server knows the persecution in store for them during the following two hours of their lives. One only hopes that obliging the pains-in-the-ass will result in a good tip. Luckily, Mr. Finkel and Mr. Goldenstein paid well for their wives' weekly sadistic entertainment. And I was able to turn the table in sufficient time to meet the hostess's expectations. *Whew!*

I eventually won without making a single mistake that evening, much to the disappointment of the two divas, although they truly appreciated good service. I was also pretty clever. For instance, while saying, "Of course," to the foursome's request for extra sauce on the Lobster Fra Diavolo, another special order, I knew there wasn't a chance I would consider asking Jonesy for more sauce on a Saturday night. For one thing, that particular dish was swimming in sauce.

Instead, when I placed the plate of steaming lobster tails brimming in spicy red richness in front of Mrs. Goldenstein, I announced, "Okay, here's the Lobster Fra Diavolo with extra sauce." It was a strategy that worked every time.

The women hugged me as they departed. It was only sport, after all.

Back in the kitchen, Jonesy usually took his anger out on only one server per night and managed to be somewhat cordial to the rest of us. Lucky for me, Jonesy was a breast man. I *think* he liked me, anyway. I'm from the neighborhood, so I hesitate to say we had a minimalist bond. My "Jonesy" nickname was Big Tit Val (to distinguish me from another server named Val, short for Valentina in her case).

On one other particular Saturday evening, Ivy was in the hot seat. She accepted an order for garlic bread (not a menu item) and attempted to inconspicuously slip the order into the kitchen. You couldn't get much past Jonesy and in a matter of seconds you could hear him yelling, "Get the fuck out of here with this garlic bread. Do you know how busy we are tonight? Don't tell me the fucking customer requested it; I know you talked them into it."

Desperate, Ivy pulled me aside and asked me to place the order for her. This was only successful on nights when I wore a lower-cut blouse. I waited a few minutes and casually went into the kitchen carrying a basket of sliced Italian bread, walked behind the line, touched Jonesy on his shoulder and said, "Jonesy, I know how busy we are tonight, but do you think you could please throw in an order of garlic bread? It's for Mr. and Mrs. Llanarch."

Jonesy looked directly into my cleavage, smiled and said, "Look at those fucking tits. Okay guys, make her the fucking garlic bread." I leaned in and kissed his sweaty, desperately-in-need-of-a-shave cheek and thanked him. As I reached the door to the dining room he yelled from behind, "And don't think I don't know this garlic bread is for fucking Ivy, that motherfucker."

Thanks to this exercise I carved myself a reputation and was granted favor among my co-workers, especially when it came to ordering our own staff meals. As female servers, we were allowed to order pasta or salad free of charge before the beginning of each dinner shift. All other menu items were available to us at half price...that is, if the kitchen obliged us. Ordering dinners did not guarantee the guys in the kitchen would be willing to make it. If they were in bad moods, they'd simply refuse. Rat to Micky? Not a mother-fucking chance!

Enter my triple-Ds. Whenever the kitchen shot down a menu request, the girls sent me in there like the fixer. And most often, I returned to our dinner table victorious with shitake mushrooms or grilled Dover sole in hand. Hey, there were people who prostituted themselves for much lesser—and much greater—things in life. Manipulating Jonesy and the boys with a few inches of cleavage was a small price to pay for seafood and heroism.

By the way, the Tavern's only male waiter, John Travolta Jerry, as well as the bartenders never seemed to have this problem, nor did they ever need to tighten their pants to get what they wanted for staff dinner. And their dinners were on the house.

This brings to mind another Tavern classic: the "sexual harassment training" story, which took place the same time the Anita Hill/Clarence Thomas proceedings were in the news, bringing workplace harassment to the forefront. Restaurants were far from office environments where harassment took on less conspicuous proposals. I knew both well. For this training, all Tavern staff members were required to attend the sexual harassment session presented by the restaurant's insurance company. So, they scheduled the presentation between lunch and dinner shifts, and we were all forewarned to be on our best behaviors. Most of us complied, with the exception of Roach, the busboy.

Midway through our training, Roach excused himself to the bathroom and was gone for about five minutes. When he returned to the session in progress with a glass of ice in one hand and a Coke bottle in the other, he approached his seat in the back row next to Chrissy. He leaned over and whispered to her, "Hey, Chris, do me a favor? Would you mind grabbing the pen from my left pocket?"

Accommodatingly, Chrissy reached in. She didn't find a pen. Instead, what she inadvertently discovered was a huge hard-on pushed to the inside of Roach's pants pocket. Roach was laughing so hard in the silent way you did in the back of a classroom that he was actually crying. The trainer had to pause the presentation to regain the group's attention, unaware of what inspired the commotion. Chrissy was a good sport about it. For Christ's sake, we were all good sports.

Years later, after he retired, I ran into Jonesy at a doctor's office. By then he had to be in his mid-seventies. His face was still badly in need of a shave. The first thing he said to me after our greeting was, "I'm here for my dick; I can't get it up anymore."

I was actually taken aback for a moment by the vulgarity. I mean, I was in daytime professional mode. Looking over my shoulder to see who else may have heard Jonesy's crude description of his medical problem, I began to tell him about the book I was writing about our Tavern days. Toothless and smiling up at me from his chair, he waved his hand dismissively and said, "Ah, those motherfuckers!"

Louie's Backyard

We were cleaning up after a Thursday lunch shift when Rachael and Francesca approached me about joining them on a trip to the Keys. Francesca was living with someone, but it wasn't working out. Rachael and Frankie were finally separated, though he had refused to sign divorce papers for fear she would be entitled to half his pension. I was single at the moment.

"I can't afford to go right now," I instantly answered. "But thanks for inviting me," as I wiped down the espresso machine udders with a warm, damp cloth.

"Val, all you'll need is some spending money," Rachael stressed. "Louie and those guys who sit on Table 25 every Thursday are paying for the whole thing."

"Forget it!" I dismissed the idea as I stocked more coffee cups on the shelf. "They're like a hundred years old and I don't even know them."

I must admit, it sounded glamorous to be whisked away to Key West, all expenses paid, for a long weekend. If I'm being honest, I mildly envied Dana and the other girls' jet-setting, customer-funded lifestyles...and here I was, finally getting an invite. Then I thought about Louie and his cronies, who I had not yet met at that point in my Tavern career. Though I didn't know them personally, I had seen them in the restaurant and didn't find any of these guys attractive.

Plus, I was pretty sure they were all married. As I momentarily entertained the idea of going, my buzzkill practicality set in. Who would I be indebted to for such an indulgence, and what would be my payment?

Rachael and Fran kept trying to convince me to go. "We might go on Louie's yacht," they dangled. The idea of the boat was starting to sway me. I needed to consult my voices of reason—my homegirls and non-Tavern besties since kindergarten, August and Elaina, for advice.

August: "You know one of those old men is going to try to hook up with you. I wouldn't go. Absolutely not."

Elaina: "Hmm. The yacht is my Achilles' heel, but, no, I couldn't do it. You don't even know them."

That settled that for the moment and I declined Rachael and Francesca's invitation. I just couldn't go under the circumstances. That's when Rachael informed me that my airline ticket had already been purchased.

"*By whom*?" I urged, feeling a bit played.

"Louie," Fran answered casually as if this was totally commonplace.

Though I had never been introduced to Louie, I knew I had to summon the courage to give him the thank-you-but-no-thank-you, I-don't-feel-comfortable-accepting speech.

The following Thursday, Louie was sitting at the downstairs bar having a glass of Ruffino Ducale. I approached him from behind and politely tapped his shoulder. If I had to guess, I'd say Louie was in his sixties then. He was a short guy who looked like he could pass for Joe Pesci's brother (he hated when people made that connection).

"Hi, Louie. I'm Valerie. Can I talk to you for a second?"

"Sure honey," he answered before lifting his eyes to meet

mine. He was peeling off a $100 bill from his rubber-banded wad of money and laid it on the bar as a tip for Big Bud. "What can I do for you?"

"I wanted to talk to you about the trip to Florida."

I detected a little confusion in his eyes, but we'd never been introduced before this moment, so it could have been the fact that he didn't know who the hell I was. He listened.

"It was so generous of you to buy my ticket, but I don't know you guys very well and I don't feel comfortable accepting a trip," I explained. I could hear myself speaking the words, but it felt as though they came from a ventriloquist somewhere behind me. *It's the Tavern, Val, not your corporate job! You sound like a prude.*

He had a quick mind that gravitated toward the shadier side of things, and he wasn't stupid.

"Listen honey," he interrupted, placing his hand on my shoulder, "there are no strings attached. If you want to come along to Key West, we'd love to have you. There's an odd number of us going, so no pressure. It should be a fun time."

I believed him. And by the end of our chat, I told him to count me in.

The origin of this trip was a bit gray to me. I wasn't sure who initiated it and who was trying to use who. I was simply going for the adventure...because I could.

Louie and I ended up sitting together on the connecting flight from Miami to Key West. I learned he was recently divorced. He told me he loved the Keys for fishing. I asked what he did for a living, and he told me about his sign manufacturing company located in New Jersey, and how he built it from scratch. Over rum and Cokes replenished by our flight attendant, Louie shared that he was still amazed by the company's success considering he had spent a short time of his adolescence in a juvenile detention center. "Sometimes I don't know how I got from there to here, honey," he contemplated aloud, shaking his head. We talked about the restaurant and how long I had been working there. The trip was already going by quickly, and I finally got the courage to ask him about the ticket. I leaned over my first-class window seat toward him and quietly probed, "I have a question if you don't mind, Louie. Fran and Rachael were a little sketchy about the details of this trip when they invited me to come. Would you tell me the truth about something? When I first approached you at the Tavern bar a few weeks ago, had you already purchased my ticket?"

He shook his head "no" and smiled. From that moment, he became my friend and we would remain solid friends for the remainder of his time on Earth.

Louie could have written the book on *How to Win Friends and Influence People*, but he didn't have to. Everyone who knew him knew his big-spending nature firsthand. Perhaps the result of a short man complex, thought by some. Either way, Louie blacklisted "friends" who refused to let him pick up a check, and that meant not being invited to Louie's infamous parties. He loved hosting elaborate dinners at his favorite restaurants, or as he did on our first night in Key West at the well-known Louie's Backyard, coincidentally.

Louie's Backyard is still a Key West must-try restaurant, and I understood why the minute we walked in. There was something magical about it. The entire dining area was outdoors on tiered decks that overlooked the Gulf of Mexico. Besides the stars, the only other illumination came from hundreds of tiny patio lights that trimmed the perimeter of each tier, and flickering tabletop candles. The food was exquisite, with fish just reeled in from the waters beneath us, and the desserts were even better—huge bowls of crème brûleé filled with fresh berries the size of acorns. To date, it's the best brûleé I've ever eaten. The evening was an icebreaker for our group of seven. And it was there when I discovered the real reason Rachael wanted to go on this trip: she secretly had a crush on Louie's younger brother, Donnie, who came along. Donnie wasn't a Tavern regular and by far the best looking of the bunch. He was aloof. In spite of this, his presence helped me answer why the girls were so persistent about me joining them... If Rachael was successful in rendezvousing with Donnie, then Francesca would have had to go it alone with the guys, or worse—be vulnerable to advances from one of them for a double date situation. So, they had asked me to come along. It was the old "safety in numbers" strategy.

The next day while the guys fished from Louie's Convertible Bertram yacht he kept docked there—which, by the way, I did not step foot on—Francesca, Rachael and I relaxed on the Marriott's private beach. I guess it wasn't a total loss. Around lunchtime a barefoot, blond-mopped waiter in a floral short-sleeved shirt walked through the sand, balancing a tray of jumbo fresh shrimp cocktail, shucked oysters and prawns.

"Are you Mr. B's girls?" he queried, referring to Louie's last name. We couldn't see his eyes behind the iridescent aviators he wore, but he was surely cute. He could have easily been a lifeguard with his seasoned, even golden tan that reached the tips of his bare toes, and sun-bleached arm and leg hair.

We looked at each other with surprise and curiosity.

"Yes, I guess we are," Francesca beamed. "And who are

you?"

"My name is Brian and I'll be your server this afternoon. Mr. B. has also instructed me to bring over a bottle of Dom Pérignon, or would you ladies prefer Perrier-Jouët instead? Or can our bartender make you something else?"

We opted for the Perrier-Jouët.

When he returned with the floral champagne bottle on ice and three flutes, he informed us that our beachside massages were scheduled to begin at 4 p.m. and asked if that time slot would be acceptable. *And to think that I almost bailed on this trip.*

This was living, I thought. I couldn't wait to report back to August and Elaina. It was so fun to be wined and dined.

Still, I wondered if there were any expectations. Our male counterparts appeared to be having fun, and maybe keeping hope alive for getting lucky after enough alcohol. There wasn't enough booze on that island for me, though I enjoyed hanging out with them. They were actually funny.

I offered to pay my way whenever the opportunity arose so no one would get the wrong idea. But Fran and Rachael pulled me aside and schooled me. "Stop offering to pay!" they scolded. "They might take us up on it!" I took their grooming and figured I had already made my point, anyway. These guys had become accustomed to the reciprocity of wining and dining women, and they were not at all used to women reaching for a check, nor did they like giving up control.

As the weekend progressed, there were a few awkward moments. Donnie, Louie's brother, skipped a few outings, leaving Rachael a bit disappointed and resulting in an even boy/girl count at meals. I did what I do best to ease the tension: told funny stories. The guys got a big kick out of me, and playing the funny girl not only broke the ice, but underscored my position as a gracious tag-along. Francesca was unaffected. She was solely interested in an all-expenses-paid trip to anywhere to escape real life for a little while.

On our last night, the guys went out to dinner without us, leaving us to fend for ourselves. I sensed a bit of spitefulness or maybe disappointment when they realized they weren't likely to score. It was just as well for the three of us. We tooled around Duval Street shopping and laughing. On the flight home the next morning, there was a weird tension, though Louie and I chatted fairly comfortably.

When we returned to the Tavern, none of our co-workers believed our trip was platonic. Truthfully, the guys who got the most skin, you might say, were our masseuses. I'm sure our traveling companions were a bit disappointed with the outcome. In fact, they scheduled a do-over, so to speak. They already planned a Key West reunion dinner party at Louie's house.

The next time we met was in Louie's actual backyard, at his home in Cape May, N.J. He cooked an amazing five-course dinner during which Louie, the guys, Rachael, Francesca and I consumed a case of Taittinger Rosé champagne. We laughed about the funniest moments on the Key West trip and avoided mentioning the awkward ones. If the men had hoped for anything romantic to happen this time around, they probably should have limited the champagne. We were all a little sloppy and could have used some cold showers. Instead, we opted for Louie's in-ground pool...sans our clothes. We hadn't brought bathing suits along, so what else were we supposed to do? There in Louie's backyard, I had my first ever skinny-dipping experience. I would have preferred a pool full of guys resembling Brian, our Key West beach server.

The funny thing is, I have no recollection of what any of the guys' bodies looked like. I was cockeyed drunk, for one thing. The only person whose body I can clearly recall is Rachael's. We learned that day that she had been on the diving team in high school, and apparently, she was still very skilled at jackknifing. Almost unbelievably, not even a kiss had been exchanged among any of us. For these guys, watching us disrobe (if they were even able to see straight) and dive into the pool was a big enough thrill and solidified the ridiculous Thursday lunch tips for a long time to come.

Santa Klausman

Abe Klausman was enigmatic.

When I first arrived at the Tavern, I marveled at how all of the young, independent girls could afford beautiful, designer leather handbags from Gucci and Louis Vuitton, and expensive Movado and Cartier watches, while I was struggling to pay back student loans, my rent, a car payment, insurance, and credit card bills.

What I never expected to hear from a Tavern girl was that the bag she carried or the watch she wore were knockoffs, *but really good ones.* Even Phyllis might have had a hard time discerning one of the illegitimate Gucci or Vuitton bags. Yep. They came straight out of the trunk of a Cadillac. That part of it was easy for me to understand. After all, some of my family's appliances came from a trunk, albeit the back of a Chevy.

There was this guy named Jamesy Head, who my parents knew from the old neighborhood. He had a big head, obviously. He sported a mustache that looked like it was drawn on his face with a black Sharpie marker and didn't match his dyed brown hair. He talked like he was on speed while chain-smoking filterless cigarettes at our kitchen table. He talked so much and so quickly that he always seemed to have a buildup of dried white saliva in the corners of his mouth. I remember my younger sisters and I imitating his smoking gestures behind his back and giggling out of control whenever he would come over to our house to ply his wares.

Jamesy's visits were usually by invitation when word got out that my parents were in the market for something like a window air conditioner or a toaster oven. Someone would say, "Call Jamesy. He's got some nice ones." And he'd appear at our door on a late Saturday morning. I think his "customers" even bought items of clothing from Jamesy's car on occasion, like these corduroy turquoise, car-length jackets that I swear every mom on our street owned.

In my neighborhood, it was no big deal to make purchases from Jamesy's trunk. It was just like buying fruit from a huckster's truck. No one thought anything of it. There was no clandestine behavior when he'd walk my dad out to peruse the goods in the rear of his Monte Carlo on a sunny fall afternoon, after what seemed like six cups of black coffee. Of course, he was also offered Entenmann's cake that my mom bought for the occasion, but he opted for his cigarettes instead.

What really surprised me about the Tavern girls' trunk shopping was the fact that most of the girls weren't from South Philly, they just ended up there. Additionally, I was shocked to learn they *admittedly* donned knockoffs. *What? This materialistic bunch is openly sporting faux Chanel and Fendi!* It was acceptable to everyone but a girl named Shelly (more on her later), for one reason and one reason only…these items were gifts from the harmless and beloved Abe Klausman, and Shelly wasn't interested in making true friendships with our regulars, nor was she interested in knockoffs.

Abe was a seemingly lonely man and a Monday night regular at the Tavern. I first met him around Christmastime.

The December holidays at the Tavern added festivity to my life when I was removed from most of the customs I had known as a kid. By that time, most of my family had moved to Florida and I was living a single lifestyle. Christmas Eves were the most special memories of my childhood—everything from the shrimp over linguine we traditionally ate each year at my grandmother Josie's house, where there had to be twenty of us sitting at card tables assembled throughout the little row home, to the mystique of attending midnight mass when I was old enough, to returning home to a dark house illuminated only by the twinkling colorful Christmas tree lights, to my mom's famous homemade butter cookies, family visits, and especially my parents' happy moods and reprieve from their problems. Sadly, when my parents' marriage died, so, too, did these traditions.

Each Christmas at the Tavern, Micky and our stock and inventory manager, accurately and warmly called Deaf Eddie, would take out the tall ladder to hang three gigantic metallic balls with red bows above the upstairs bar, and painstaking strings of soft white lights along the perimeters of the entryways. Real pine wreaths hung outside every window with big, red velvet bows. The fireplace in the upstairs dining room housed smoldering logs exclusively this time of year.

An ongoing stream of customers celebrating with colleagues came and went, and there was always music. Every Friday afternoon during the holiday season, we would pass out lyrics to Christmas songs and the entire staff on duty and every customer would carol in the downstairs dining room. I'm not sure how the caroling tradition started, but it had become a favored new Christmas tradition in my early twenties.

One December night, Abe and his attorney friend Mel

Klein were seated at my table. Abe was as consistent as he was dry; he never swayed from a chopped salad, Dover sole with lemon and capers sauce, and a Strega (flambé) with his decaf espresso. And he was always quick with a Yiddish-inspired one-liner.

After dinner he said to me, "Come out to the car and pick out a watch and a handbag." I wondered what the hell this guy was talking about. *Was he a distributor?* Why I never associated this with the trunk shopping of my childhood was because Abe lived on Philly's Main Line. In addition, I was stunned when I learned that Abe was a "bookie." I had no idea there were non-Italian bookies, let alone those who stocked goods in the trunks of their cars. Abe also had a very high-end clientele of doctors and accountants. To that my dad always said, "Val, everyone puts their pants on the same way in the morning." *Maybe.* But, apparently, some wore a smarter pair of slacks from Brooks Brothers and others a pair of jeans from Passyunk Avenue.

While I was in the fourth grade at the Annunciation of the Blessed Virgin Mary school, for the adults in my life, playing street numbers with a "bookie" was as commonplace as going to the corner grocery store for a loaf of bread and some lunch meat. In fact, our neighborhood "number writer," Shank, had the key to my grandmother Mary's house to use her phone to call in the bets to his *boss*.

"Bookie" is slang for *bookmaker*; someone who takes illegal bets mostly on sporting events. For years, in Philly anyway, the daily number was drawn based on horse racing at a well-known track…somewhere. It was completely acceptable and understood even by us kids when an older family member would send us to ask the bookie, "What was leading?" This meant they wanted to know the first of the three-digit winning numbers for that day. Bets were always taken before the final number was announced and cash payouts were made to winners. I never fully grasped how calculations were made or how the winning numbers were selected. All I *did* know was that my dad's number was 528. Hence, if "fives were leading" on a day when he "played the number," he was anxiously optimistic he had a shot at winning.

People tended to bet money (for as little as a dime in the 70s), on their favorite numbers or a number derived from a dream. There was always one family member, mostly a grandmother or a great aunt, who held the tattered dream book that translated symbols conjured by the mind while sleeping into meanings and correlating numbers. Playing the numbers was so much a part of our subculture that my fourth grade classmate, Annamaria Donatucci, once brought "bookie paper" to school for show-and-tell. Her dad was a number writer and bookie paper was dissolvable rice paper used to record the bets in the unfortunate circumstance of being caught by the police for illegal gambling. Bookies could then simply eat the paper and *voila*—it would dissolve in their mouths, and all evidence would be destroyed. I wish I had a photo to commemorate the gaggle of grade-schoolers in blue plaid uniforms huddled around the janitor's bucket with Sisters Georgine and Paula, watching bookie paper dissolve.

In 1972, the government finally caught on to what a great gig this was and introduced the Pennsylvania Lottery. Though these two ends of the gambling spectrum coexisted for a while, the state-run lotteries eventually put the number writers out of business.

Back to the Tavern. Sweet Abe was a friend to many

of the girls, and often treated us to tickets for shows at the casinos. In fact, the first and only time I saw Frank Sinatra perform live was with Abe at Bally's in Atlantic City. As Frank, who was, by then, in the autumn of his life, swooned *Mack the Knife*, he missed a few key words. Abe leaned into me and said, "Oy vey—with all his money, they can't get him a teleprompter?"

That same night, Abe won $50,000 playing craps. They escorted him into a private room to count out his winnings and he let me come along. I had never seen that much cash in my life. That's the night Abe bought me a beautiful cognac-colored suede suit. Given my trepidations about receiving, I would have normally felt uncomfortable accepting it. Again, my mind asked, *What would I need to do in return?* Though I loved him dearly, I wasn't the least bit attracted to Abe, besides the forty-year age difference. It was lucky for me that he presented all of us with gifts from his winnings that night. Dana's friend Darla had gotten a beautiful REAL Chanel mink purse, and a girl named Aubrey, who only worked at the Tavern for about a year, was given a 14-karat gold charm bracelet. If memory serves, I believe Aubrey was willing to go a little further with Abe for all the prizes. Abe was a lonely soul and we made him feel, well, not so lonely. It *was* a give and take exchange.

Other than providing Tavern girls with accessories—and indirectly Elaina, August, and my mom and sisters, who benefited from the handbags and watches, too—Abe kept somewhat of a low profile. But the IRS eventually caught up with him. He ended up doing two years at a Federal camp in the middle of Pennsylvania, along with some politicians and other white-collar guys who also misinterpreted the law.

Being loyal friends with Abe, a group of us journeyed out to visit him from time to time. On one occasion, Ivy, Chrissy, Francesca, the restaurant's bookkeeper Nancy, and I piled into Phyllis's Mercedes on a cold Sunday morning. We had to leave very early in order to arrive in time for visiting hours. Halfway there, we pulled into a roadside diner for breakfast. We might as well have been in the backwoods of Mississippi or any other people-less, rural part of the country for that matter, as Ivy attempted to order egg whites and skim milk with her coffee. The waitress had no idea you could have eggs without the yolks. Wearing her Salvatore Ferragamo pumps, Phyllis stepped in and said, "Ivy, we're in the middle of bum-fuck America and we're going to miss visiting hours at the prison. So could you please order something off the menu?"

Ivy complied. The waitress was rapt, especially after receiving a $50 tip on a $25 check. And Abe was so happy to see us. We were like every other extended family, functioning through dysfunction.

CO-D

"Hey, can you give me a ride home?" Melanie yelled down from the third-floor dressing room.

"Sure! Are you ready to go?" I bellowed back upstairs. "The snow is coming down hard."

Micky had to close the restaurant early because of a heavy snowstorm, a rarity. I was excited to get home before 10 p.m. on a Monday night for a change.

Standing 6' tall with rich, sand-colored hair and blue eyes filled with clarity, Melanie had the physical makings of a runway model and the brains of a doctor. Actually, she was on her way to becoming a pediatrician. Of my Tavern friends, Melanie and I had the distinction of sharing our entire tenures there together. We also shared a birth month and year, and the memory of driving a U-Haul across the country to take Mel to grad school in Wyoming.

I did all the driving on that trip and didn't mind it, except for Mel's cat Bizarre resting on my head the entire way. I am highly allergic to cats. One errant hair can turn my eye whites into jellyfish. Thank goodness Melanie's mom thought to push a Sudafed into my mouth as we shoved off with cargo packed so tightly from floor to ceiling in the truck's box that Bizarre had no better sleeping alternative...or else I'd have been in anaphylactic shock before leaving the Keystone State.

Mel's amazing brain, being capable of both science and

art, ensured there was no lull in conversation in the U-Haul, except when we opted for quiet. For that matter, there was never a shortage of conversation during our seven-block drive home from the Tavern, either. For many nights we sat parked, talking for hours in front of Mel's apartment building before she finally went inside.

Swapping our heels for our boots, Melanie and I cut through the heavily falling sideways snow to my little Hyundai hatchback parked in the municipal lot.

"Could you believe that Billy Joel eluded me again?" I asked jokingly.

We both laughed out loud. Mel's laugh was more like a guffaw.

"You mean now you'll have to postpone breaking up with your passionless boyfriend and your move to the Hamptons?" she asked sarcastically.

I grinned. She was funny. It was true. Not the part about moving to the Hamptons. Pragmatic me had returned to my body and the notion of dating Billy Joel had left me for the moment.

"That's exactly what I was thinking. Ha, ha! What can I say? Seriously though, Mel, I'm really ready to end my relationship with Alex. I'm glad you needed a lift home because I wanted to get your thoughts on what I plan to say to him. Sorry that you are a captive audience and a trusted passenger. How I torture you! It isn't fair payment for the seven-block ride home."

"Sure, it is. I know exactly what I am signing up for."

Therein lies the epitome of living in the present, and a resounding message imparted to me by Melanie, though it would take some years before the concept really took root in my operating system.

Melanie had a nickname for me back then. It was "Co-D."

I am a recovering codependent. It's not my fault.

You see, the stars aligned in such a way when I arrived on Earth that I landed carrying a big sack equipped for hauling loads of responsibility with added room for accumulating guilt. In it were Virgo peculiarities and self-imposed guidelines for perfection. A large set of imposing family values. Catholicism. A dose of extremely intelligent relatives who set the bar high. A few addictive family members, and a ginormous Italian American, tight-knit community whose members loved passionately, but with condition and judgment.

The family inheritance included the life stations of two loving grandmothers, both first-generation Americans born of immigrant parents. Both had lived through the Great Depression and WWII, had worked in sweatshops (unless you count occasionally running numbers for bookies as a job), and both rose above the disgrace of bad husbands. Added to that was my parents' inability to successfully manage finances, causing my sisters and I to view our lives through a sort of "black sheep" lens among our extended family.

All these influences coalesced into the huge behavioral responsibility of being pleasing, extremely conscientious, such a good daughter, niece, student, sister, employee... AND girlfriend. An overwhelming feeling of obligation to others that sometimes came at my own expense.

At first I was offended by Melanie's assessment of me as "codependent." It felt judgmental when she couldn't understand why paying my dad's security deposit, and first and last month's rent for his apartment when he was broke was the "right" thing to do. It felt unkind to do anything less, even though the situation had caused a hardship for me. *Melanie just doesn't understand my family dynamic or my Italian American subculture,* I thought. Tough love was a heartless concept in our world.

Later, I remember reading somewhere that codependency is a circular relationship in which one person needs the other person, who in turn, needs to be needed. To the contrary, I was, by all accounts, self-reliant. Handling things with aplomb was a coping mechanism that propelled me through childhood and young adulthood, so the notion of codependency didn't resonate for a while.

Subconsciously, however, for all of my giving, I *was* getting something back: validation that I was ever so capable of carrying someone else's (sometimes everyone else's) shit in that big bag of responsibility…until I wasn't. *Hence, my overdue breakup with Alex.* I would eventually come to know on a cellular level how not living in one's truth was the sole cause for resentment.

The upside of my upbringing was my father's hilarity and my mother's ability to laugh. It provided a humorous window for viewing life and a common denominator I share with my sisters, albeit our personalities are each very different from one another.

Humor is fundamental to my framework, but it is not a substitute for good decision-making. Come to think of it, the problem-solving training I received as a child came primarily by way of a saying, a song, or a line from a movie that was used to provide distraction, offer a quick remedy, or kindly dismiss you when other responsibilities took precedence. Few adults in my family ever sat us kids down for a meaningful, sober, non-judgmental pros and cons discussion about any serious problem.

Having a bad day? "Even the subway's in a hole. Even the chorus girls are kicking!" my mom would offer cheerfully while prepping dinner. Experiencing a conundrum? Grandmom Josie reincarnated Barbra Streisand's "On a Clear Day You Can See Forever." Embroiled in gossip? "Don't shit where you eat," Grandmom Mary affirmed. Got an undeserved bad grade? "Can't fight City Hall," Aunt Angela would offer to move on. Need some future incentive? "Everything's coming up tulips for me and for you," my father belted in his best Ethel Merman impersonation.

Even now, when Ivy and I discuss the challenges du jour, she'll ask, "What would your grandmothers have said to that, Valley Girl?"

I guess the stickier or more uncomfortable a situation was to confront, music and idioms offered levity and some underlying perspective.

Decades later, I listened to an audiobook by Deepak Chopra during a drive down the shore. I had a revelation about these expressions that hit me like a bag of cement. The sayings and lines from movies and songs were all phrases that embodied a subliminal perception of baked-in acquiescence. This constituted a language of limitations spoken by an entire community who raised me, though they had no idea. I had never considered the continual stream of mildly annoying but endearing adages as a throwing-in-the-towel (pun intended) fundamental outlook. It explained an awful lot about my initial culture shock at the Tavern, among other aha moments.

While my mom parented mostly from the gut, I always felt her loving guidance, as well as the deep love of my father. I also fondly remember heart-to-heart chats with a few of my aunts, including happy memories of talks with my dad's sister at her kitchen table about budgeting wisely or the importance of landing a good job and self-reliance. I especially recall having many one-on-one conversations with my dear Aunt Angela, my Godmother, that were brimful of honesty, reality, and soundness. I was often blown away by her open-mindedness. She was born in 1937 and I'm quite certain I never saw a Buddhist book among her Harlequin romance novels or Sue Grafton mysteries. While thinking back to her attitude and philosophy, she personified the art of bearing witness and held a somewhat avant-garde understanding of energy as a life force. I still summon memories of her advice in times of contemplation on things like being lied to, forgiveness, and her forthright and loving acknowledgement of one's shortcomings as just that.

Of my other family members, someone who was perhaps the least expected to administer a dose of resonant insight was my God*father*, Uncle Frank. He was brilliant, a classically gifted writer, and he suffered from schizophrenia. However, in moments of clarity he imparted words of great poignancy and significance in my life. In a letter he wrote me when I graduated from college, he said:

> I watched you grow into a beautiful young lady, warm, personable and caring. Now it is your graduation day and I don't know how to tell you how deeply proud I am of you—of your accomplishments and talents. And you did it, for the most part, by yourself.
>
> Actually, we are similar in so many ways, which establishes still another bond between us. The

circumstances of our lives, and even our talents are the same. I am a great believer in the fulfillment of the self with God's help—the rising above adverse circumstances to become the person whom God intended you to be. I have heard it said that a human being's worth is determined by the number of things that a human being can do without. I truly believe this and also that deprivation is the greatest builder of character in an individual.

Whatever else you may forget about me, remember always that I love you.

Uncle Frank

I wished I could remain mindful of his words during moments of insecurity, and I wished I could have embraced Aunt Ang's approach to life earlier instead of taking things so personally. *Someday I will.* I had wasted so much time and energy with Alex. And why? Because I felt the need to prove something and a determination to overcome lower expectations. There was no doubt this was borne of my big bag of Co-D components.

"Val, this is literally the fourth time you've told me you're breaking up with Alex," Mel reminded me with doubt in her voice as we slowly navigated the narrow, snow-covered streets of South Philly.

"Yes, but this time I mean it. I woke up the other day and it was like I got clunked on the head, jarring me into clarity. All of a sudden, it was so obvious that I didn't need his approval for anything. What was I doing waiting for his acknowledgement of something—*anything*—good about me? That I am funny or smart or a good cook, or a great girlfriend…"

"Don't forget HOT, too! Don't you see how the men at the Tavern gravitate to you?"

I smiled. "Thanks, but no. Dana, now she's the ultimate man magnet."

"Okay, whatever," Mel yielded, rolling her eyes. "So, what shifted for you?"

"Everything. For one, his admonishment the other day for getting a B- for his English paper…"

Mel interrupted, "You mean to tell me that asshole had the audacity to berate you for HIS college paper that YOU wrote for HIM? The one he refused to provide you notes for? Co-D, I mean, Val, seriously, why did you even agree to write his paper in the first place?"

"Because he asked me to. I wanted to be helpful. That comes easy to me."

"Yeah! When you've had the luxury of reading the assignment materials!" Mel shouted, infuriated. "And 'NO' is a full sentence!" she affirmed with complete conviction. "Aside from this blatant egregiousness, you were saying… something shifted for you that made you FINALLY feel ready to move on. Please share!"

"The other night he hinted about getting engaged. I think the prospect of spending the rest of my life unfulfilled was like cold water running down my back. You know, when I met Alex I thought I was aligning with someone worldly because he was born in England and he seemed to have more life experience, as naïve as that sounds. I thought he was someone with character. Someone with values. That's the superiority he portrays to the outside world. But when I realized he is an imposter, I became completely turned off. I wish I could take everyone on their word. Sometimes I have to exhaust all possibilities and give people every benefit of the doubt before I can move on. And when I do, I'm good with it."

"Clearly. Oh, and one other annoying fact: deflecting blame, lacking empathy, and gaslighting are textbook narcissistic traits," Melanie emphasized sternly.

"That, too. Ha! Ha! On the upside, trying to prove myself to Alex propelled me to teaching myself to drive a stick shift, beating him to graduation, and landing a great job in marketing. So, there's that. I guess I've finally realized we're not aligned, and especially not in character."

"I think what you've accomplished makes you realize that you don't need him, and certainly not his emotional abuse. There's no turning back from that awareness," she offered soberly.

"Besides all that, I REALLY want to have hot sex with someone," I gushed.

We laughed out loud.

BAR BOYS

While the Tavern boys and girls played nicely together in social settings, there was a definitive chasm between us as employees. The bar served as a line of demarcation just as the kitchen did. The girls worked the dining room and the boys tended bar, with one exception—John Travolta Jerry did both. We servers undoubtedly had access to making the most money in the restaurant of any other staff position, though the bartenders did pretty well, too. Like the kitchen staff, the bartenders sometimes pulled rank, and that usually happened at the service end of the bar where we picked up drinks for our seated customers. And there were times we were made to wait, and wait, and wait for our table's drinks… if you didn't kiss some bar ass. Cleavage was a moot point with these guys. They were too busy with customers standing three deep shouting drink orders at them.

Waiting for a martini or a bottle of pinot grigio for more than the allotted five minutes could really mess up a server's timing and easily cause a ripple effect of negative circumstances. As I mentioned, being late to pick up your food got you a bad rep with the kitchen even though that was the purpose of the food runner. And, not turning your tables quickly enough garnered you a bad rep with the hostess, even though she, too, could clearly see when the bar was holding up service.

Slow to deliver drinks to party-minded customers could result in a bad tip. Eventually word would travel to Phyllis in the office about your poor waitressing ability, and then it was doomsday—banished to the worst two-table station for a while, plus granting license for co-workers to stigmatize you. It did not matter if one of the servers was in med school carrying a 4.0. If you were relegated to a two-table station, you were seen as being as dumb as a doorknob and subject to insult. The kitchen guys and bartenders jumped on that bandwagon whenever it passed.

We servers were obliged to pay each bartender $10 a shift for their service and, in fairness, they deserved at least that. One of the older fixtures behind the bar, Bernie, was a confirmed widower who had a full head of wiry silver hair, dark-rimmed glasses and appeared at least fifteen years younger than a septuagenarian. If judging by his permanent facial expression, one might assume Bernie suffered from chronic constipation. He was miserable. But, if you upped his nightly dole by a mere $3, you were guaranteed better service. Regardless, he rarely cracked a smile unless it was in sarcasm and mockery.

Somehow, while chatting with Bernie one slow Monday evening, we discovered that his nephew and my little niece were the same age and both loved to visit Chuck E. Cheese. He had no children of his own and worshiped this little boy. So, we made plans to meet there with the kids one Sunday afternoon. The Tavern was closed on Sundays. Though I dreaded the thought of spending time with Bernie, to my surprise, he was a generous soul. He was lonely, too.

My father repeatedly told me that every person, regardless of his or her outward appearance, has an interesting story to tell if you let them. He understood that innately, though he rarely allowed others to do the storytelling. He was the master at that after all, and no one seemed to mind because it was a guaranteed comedy hour whenever he took center stage.

I have proven my father's theory true countless times in my life, and Bernie offered another example of someone who had a story to tell. Upon getting to know him, I'd learn he was an expert woodworker and responsible for making all of the Tavern's dining room wall embellishments by hand.

Rumor had it that Bernie's wife was institutionalized with a mental illness early in their marriage, which left him bitter. I could understand that. I never attempted to broach the marriage subject at Chuck E. Cheese, but Bernie alluded to it. This was the unadulterated foundation for our friendship. Hence, our little stints of lousy pizza and watching two toddlers' subterfuge in a ball pit helped keep my waitressing ability in good standing as far as delivering drinks was concerned when Bernie tended bar.

Now, when Big Bud was behind the bar, he offered a more expressive drink service, especially after having a few himself. Like his name suggests, he was 6'4" tall, and about 3' in diameter. He was a bit of a mess; loud, but harmless. On his nights off, he'd come back to the restaurant to socialize with customers and staff. He was obnoxious but benevolent while showering anyone within a foot of him with gin-infused saliva droplets when he slurred.

Another one of our bartenders, Pal Joey, was a small-framed man who bore a mild resemblance to Frank Sinatra around the nose and eyes. He was a mid-fifties family man with a full-time day job. He was a keen observer and bemused by most of the scenarios presented at the Tavern. Well, they were unilaterally funny. Although, Pal Joey's retelling them made them even funnier. He was a philosopher out of his time and loved to quote famous thinkers. It made him seem intelligent. Actually, he was.

Greg was another bartender. His claim to fame was his freakishly large penis, though I had never seen it.

And, of course, John Travolta Jerry tended bar on occasion. Cap would pull him off the floor and put him behind the bar on busy nights. But for the most part, he was one of us.

Then came Evan.

Evan presented a refreshing and adorable baby face to admire while fetching our drinks from the service bar. An Italian/Irish blend with a gorgeous crop of wavy brown hair, he had a clean cut, fair complexion, a straight nose and a fine-looking smile. He smelled like a delicious melody of fresh linen laundry detergent and sandalwood. Our chemistry was palpable almost immediately.

Evan's arrival was perfectly timed as I had just ended my relationship with Alex and I had been seriously devoid of passion. I was newly single and perhaps in rebound mode, but our flirtation was organic and cute. He didn't miss a chance to massage my shoulders whenever he'd pass me writing up a dinner order. Every time he put his hands on me from behind, I could instantly smell him, and my stomach would drop.

On Saturday nights, nearly the entire crew would go out for drinks after work at a bar up the street. Evan and I would inevitably get lost in each other, inside of our own bubble and oblivious to the laughter of our co-workers and their recitations of the night's customer encounters.

On many of those late-night drink fests after work, I

made sure to have an excuse prepared to leave alone. My trepidation? Pragmatism. I was twenty-seven and Evan was twenty-two. Though we were only five years apart, there was a huge gap in life experience between us. I was already working on my career, and he was trying to choose one. I had a formal education and he had manual skills. I was completely independent, and he still lived at home with his parents, though they were retired and preparing to move west.

Admittedly, I was also a little preoccupied by what some regulars might have thought if I started to date the new, young bartender. *Would I be taking myself off the market for other potential opportunities in the form of successful single businessmen who frequented the Tavern?* Many of the girls were attached, but intentionally skirted relationship talk, keeping the window of opportunity open in the minds of the men we served, and by extension, income. *If* there was even a chance for them, there was an even better chance of getting outrageous tips.

Thoughts had crossed my mind about what Elaina and August would think, too. The three of us accepted each other unconditionally, though they did worry a bit about me jumping into a relationship on the heels of Alex with Evan, who didn't match me on paper.

Regardless, the current of electricity connecting Evan and me was an undeniable force.

Finally, one night when my car was conveniently in the shop for brakes, I accepted a ride home with Evan. Unbeknownst to me, Alex, who had moved to New York after our breakup, decided to show up at our apartment and informed me he needed to crash there for the night. *Entitled bastard! I never thought to change the locks.* Anyway, Alex had no idea how his decision made mine to cross the line of friendship with Evan an even easier one.

With nowhere else to go at 2 a.m., we got back into Evan's car and decided to drive to Melanie's place. She graciously let us bunk on her sofa for the night and went to bed. Evan and I talked and drank and kissed until the wee hours. I felt something in my stomach that had been absent since high school. It was nice, it was entirely lustful, and it was so addictive. I craved more of him, his warm mouth and perfect embrace. Every time I thought about that night afterward, I felt a hot sweat consume my body. I couldn't wait to see him again.

A few days later though, a little panic set in. All my previous concerns began dueling with the excitement of our night on Mel's couch. Virgo girl tried to apply the brakes to slow down the progression of our unavoidable relationship… unsuccessfully.

Evan became my boyfriend for a year and a half of exhilaration. Our sexual chemistry was palpable and everyone around us felt it, too. It was my coming out.

Retelling our story sounds almost campy. We frolicked like corny lovers in a Hallmark movie, switching bathing suit bottoms beneath the transparent turquoise waters of Cancun in one scene, and picnicking under the colossal redwoods north of San Francisco in another. Together, we traveled down one coast and up the other.

When I needed some minor surgery and had to stay off my feet, Evan took me on a post-op boat ride along Baltimore's Inner Harbor while we sipped Taittinger Rosé from plastic glasses he thought to pack. He was thoughtful and affectionate, and the exact opposite of Alex. Even Elaina and August approved. We were a "thing" at the Tavern, if not *the* thing for a while. The only person who seemed to disapprove was Micky, and in a silent, disgusted kind of way whenever we expressed public affection. I wondered if he was bothered by any other relationships between staff. Certainly, Evan and I were not the first co-working couple the Tavern had seen.

In some ways, our connection represented what I think I may have wanted all along. He had great potential to make me feel complete because we had balance and were able to maintain our individual interests. It was non-threatening. Given a few more years of life experience, we could have been on even more equal footing. There were quiet times when Evan couldn't relate to my career happenings and marketing challenges. Thus, we used sex to fill any lulls in conversation. Crazy good, passionate, yummy sex—in snowstorms, limos, foreign countries, and even a log cabin. We literally couldn't get enough of each other. It was the great equalizer.

Shortly after we began dating, Evan's parents moved to Reno as planned. They had had Evan later in life; he was the youngest of ten and last remaining at home when they moved west. The deal was that Evan would remain in the South Philly house until it sold, then meet his parents in Nevada to start a career. Their relatives owned a large liquor store there that Evan was going to manage. All of this had been long settled before I came into the picture. Lucky for me, South Philly real estate was not in hot demand in the early 90s.

But eventually, it happened. Just as it felt we were getting started, the house sold and Evan had to go. Though it wasn't unforeseen, it was implausible by then. We had not counted on falling in love.

It was devastating. We weren't ready to live together in a

committed relationship and I was just gaining momentum at my new position as an assistant vice president in advertising at the bank. Back then I had never even considered moving so far from the Jersey beaches I loved. And we both knew that visiting opportunities would be limited because of the distance.

Looking back with greater awareness now, what probably attracted me most to Evan was the fact that I knew there was a clear ending from the start, as crazy as that sounds. To borrow a line from Ivy: "Our entire relationship took place inside a pair of parentheses." No commitment necessary.

The afternoon before Evan left Philadelphia, we met for a beer and he headed home to finish packing. I went to my apartment to shower and prepare our last dinner together that evening. I threw on a cute little linen dress and a pair of cowboy boots, put a few ribeye steaks in a marinade, and called Evan. It was difficult to talk without choking up.

"Hi. What time are you heading over here? Have you finished packing yet?"

"Yeah, I'm all packed. I'll be over in a little while...just finished smoking a bone and I'm lying on my bed listening to 4 Non Blondes."

His voice sounded distant already, but I could clearly hear the uncanny lyrics from "What's Up?" through the receiver.

I swallowed hard before answering and used my pinky finger to prevent the welling tears from leaving my eye sockets. "You okay? I don't want to spend our last night with only seventy-five percent of you. You know how I hate it when you're not all there."

"I'm sorry. Just feeling so confused," he admitted in a saddened voice.

"Look on the bright side," I faked. "I'll be flying out to visit you in a few months, so it's not really goodbye."

"I know. I'll be over in thirty minutes," he breathed audibly. "So...what are we having for dinner?"

"Each other?"

"I'll be over in twenty!"

What followed were several blips of relationships I wish I could erase from the diary of my life. And some I would not.

Oh, Mexico! I Just Had to Go

Evan's move marked my first meaningful heartbreak. *Not bad for twenty-eight, I guess.* After a few months of having only one or two of my twenty known endorphins working at optimal performance levels, I was tired of feeling *blah* but still devoid of desire for rebounding. Going out with the Tavern crew to one of Louie's parties or dinner with August and Elaina offered no decoy. I knew I had to do something different, but I wasn't sure what that looked like. Then, as though the Universe heard me, a new possibility emerged.

I was sitting in my apartment one evening going through the mail and came upon a homemade newsletter I subscribed to called, *The Shoestring Traveler*. On the back of the yellow, saddle-stitched, pre-Internet pamphlet was an ad that read:

Learn Spanish in one month.
$18 per day room and board in private
accommodations plus tuition.
For more information, call Isabella Llerena.

Though I was a French minor in college, learning Spanish was something I had been thinking about. There were many opportunities surfacing in international marketing with the passing of NAFTA. So, I called.

I was a little unnerved about the prospect of traveling

alone for the first time, and to a foreign country where I did not speak the language. Besides, I was going to be there for my birthday and I had never been without friends or family on my birthday in my entire life. In the pre-cell phone era, communication with my family and friends would be minimal at best. In some ways, I was really going there to hear the silence and to rediscover myself. And, hopefully learn Spanish, too.

I spent the next few weeks finagling every possible personal, vacation and sick day available to me at the bank so that I could escape for a month. I was picking up extra shifts at the Tavern to cover my expenses and the income I'd lose while in Mexico. In between, I was calling the Mexican Consulate to try to confirm the authenticity of the school. Although I had arrived at some dead ends in my research, I was at least able to verify the school's existence. La Escuela Internacional de Español had an authentic mailing address in Cuernavaca, Morelos, Mexico.

"It should be fine," the Consulate representative allayed. *Should?* The operative word.

Eight weeks later, escalating 20,000 feet above a U.S. land puzzle beneath me, I wondered what in the hell I was doing. Had I lost my mind? What if it was all a scam and I was abducted, or worse? What if my family never heard from me again?

Breathe, I told myself.

A couple of miniature bottles of California Cabernet later, I disembarked into a sea of, well, Mexicans waiting to greet their family members and friends arriving at the Mexico City International Airport. Isabella Llerena, the school's U.S. liaison who coordinated my arrangements via telephone from her home in Texas, told me a chaperone would meet me at the baggage claim bearing a sign with my name on it. I automatically envisioned an older, avuncular man.

From left to right, my eyes perused the landscape of hundreds of colorfully dressed people, most with shiny black hair. I saw no older man holding a sign with my name on it. My eye did catch two taller young men, one of whom was a handsome blend of Spaniard and Aztec. Somehow, my sixth sense told me they would be my ride before dismissing the nano thought as wishful thinking.

As I surveyed the waiting crowd in reverse, my eyes again landed on the two young men, but this time the taller one was holding up a sign that read, "Valerie Imparato." Flashing a smile, I bustled toward them, waving my free arm high and projecting a loud and Gringo-esque, "Hola! Hola! Over here. I'm Valerie. Soy Valerie Imparato."

I knew about twelve Spanish phrases in total. I had been working so much that I never had the chance to purchase a Spanish-English dictionary before the trip. Thankfully, Elaina thought to bring her 101 textbook when she gave me a lift to the Philly airport. Almost as an afterthought, she pulled the book from the back seat and offered it to me as I exited her car at the terminal.

My chaperones, Jorge and Rafael, were unphased by me. Conversely, while they looked trustworthy enough, I was completely unnerved about riding in the backseat of a 1974 Volkswagen Beetle with two strange guys, through downpouring rain on unfamiliar roads in a foreign land, for a one-and-a-half-hour drive south to Cuernavaca. Yet, there was absolutely nothing I could do or say to change my circumstances. This is what I had signed up for, as Mel would say, so I was in the hands of fate.

During the ride, I sat quietly for the most part, listening without a speck of comprehension to the banter between the two twenty-something friends in the front seat. Occasionally, after referencing my textbook's glossary, I'd attempt to ask a question of my chaperones. At last, after driving for about an hour, Jorge assured me, "Eeetz okay. We speak Eenglesh."

Although relieved, I was a little frustrated. *You mean to tell me they waited an hour into our trip to let me know they speak English, while I labor to parse together a few sentences like a stroke victim?* I honestly did not know if they were purposely not speaking to me, or so engrossed in their own conversation that they were oblivious to my presence. Then again, I was completely at their mercy.

Sometime after midnight, we turned into a residential neighborhood. It was difficult to make out the scenery in the dark through the fogged and rain-beaded back window of the Beetle. Jorge turned to me, "Wait herrre momento. We have to check out la casa."

Using my sweater sleeve, I wiped a swatch of condensation from the window so I could peer out. I saw my two chaperones chatting with what appeared to be a twelve-year-old girl peeking just her head around the front door. They returned to the car a few moments later and said, "You can stay herrre tonight. The ADDress you gave duz not exeesta. Eeetz safe herrre."

What does that mean? Is it usually unsafe here?

With no other apparent alternatives, Jorge and Rafael delivered my luggage and me to the front door. I quickly learned that the "twelve-year-old" was actually a grown but tiny woman, Nadia. She was a dentist, in fact. She had just moved into that house a few days prior but most of her furnishings had yet to meet her there. Nadia was an approved host for visiting students attending La Escuela Internacional de Español.

Nadia ushered me to a room at the far end of the long and barren house, aside from a single sofa positioned against the wall on the right. There was an empty twin bed with tossed back blankets exposing the fresh indent from a body on the underlying sheet. Hers. On the right was a set of bunk beds occupied by two sleeping children. The petite woman insisted in foreign tongue with the use of emphatic body language that I take the bed. That was the first of many wordless exchanges I had had in Mexico.

Bodily exhausted and mentally reeling, I slipped surreptitiously beneath the warm covers, fully clothed in my travel attire and wedging my handbag between my knees for fear of theft of my every dollar and peso, as well as the documents identifying me for the American Embassy if needed. I was still untrusting of my environment.

As I lay there somewhere between wakefulness and sleep, I remembered a cultural anthropology course I had taken in college and reading a book by Edward T. Hall called, *The Silent Language*, the title of which he appropriately coined for our ability to communicate without the use of words. He asserted that context plays as big a role as does body language, and I marveled at how Nadia imparted to me to take her bed. Subsequent conversations of this nature would prove to be even more remarkable.

God knows what time it was when I eventually fell asleep at last. What felt like only five minutes later, had it not been for the blinding, rising sun flooding into the room's small window, I was rudely awakened by the pounce of a small object on my leg. I sprang to a sitting position. It was a kitten. The little tan-striped fur ball was not alone. She and her little siblings and nursing mother were sharing the bedroom with us. After a few minutes, more feline family members made their way onto my bed. I was petrified that my eyes would turn to jellyfish. I had not packed my prescription eye drops.

Then I realized my handbag was still under the bed covers and muffled a laugh of self-deprecation at my unwarranted mistrust. In the 80s, the conventional travel advice for visiting a foreign country outside of resort areas was cautionary. I read that I should have worn a money belt, but that would not have looked good with the brown floral sundress that I chose for the plane ride. *Priorities.* I turned away from the cats to survey my surroundings and realized the two sleeping children to my right were little girls, Flavia and Isabella, who I would unknowingly babysit before leaving their country. Just then, I felt something wet on the sheets near my hip. One of the cats had peed on the bed. *Oh no! Will the dentist think I peed in her bed?*

Careful not to wake the girls, I tried shooing the cats away.

Back to the Spanish 101 textbook to find the words. My search in the stupid eight-page glossary offered only one option that fit the circumstance. It was "cama," which means "bed." I was on my own for the rest. Nadia must have heard me stirring about and came into the room. I looked up at her and whispered resourcefully, "*Señora, Señior Pussy Gato pee pee in me cama.*" Somehow, from the archives of my brain I must have extracted a reference from the old Warner Bros. Speedy Gonzalez cartoons.

"Oye!" she scolded. She gathered the cat family and led

them into an adjacent yard. "Pee pee" must be universal. At that, she guided me to the kitchen where she was preparing a vast breakfast. I was not hungry but politely indulged in a few items in lieu of attempting to communicate: a ham and cheese quesadilla, a yogurt smoothie, and fresh fruit, to name a few of the bountiful homemade foods set before me. It was only 6 a.m.

After I ate, I sat there trying to busy myself reading Elaina's textbook, but I could not absorb a single word on a page. I could feel the undigested breakfast like a ball of crumpled wax paper lodged in my stomach. Suddenly, my face became flushed, and my heartbeat increased as my awareness about my inability to communicate peaked. I was very far from home and all the safety it provided. I was overtired. For the first time since I was five years old, I was in the throes of a full panic attack. Hall referred to this state as "cultural anxiety."

In the nick of time, my saviors arrived. A 6' tall, blond and blue-eyed couple appeared at the top of a stairwell I had not noticed the night before when I arrived at the house.

"I am Yon and this is Pia," the guy announced in a sing-song, cartoon-ish accent. It sounded like an imitation of someone from Scandinavia. Turns out, they *were* from Scandinavia. Norway, to be exact.

Thank the blessed Lord! I immediately felt my anxiety retreat. *They speak English!* My welling tears drained back into my sinus cavities, and I smiled with great gratitude looking up at the Nordic pair.

"Hi. My name is Valley. I arrived late last night, and the address I had for my host family was incorrect. I am so relieved you speak English! I don't know a word of Spanish, which is why I'm here," I jabbered nervously with a laugh. "Can you please ask Nadia where I am supposed to go this morning?"

The couple immediately obliged and began speaking to Nadia in what sounded like beautiful Spanish to me. Then Pia turned to me and explained, "Don't worry. She'll contact your host family while we're at class this morning. We'll take you to the school."

"Thank you so much!" I turned toward Nadia and smiled. "Gracias Señora for the desayuno and cama!" "Breakfast" was also in the textbook's glossary! I gave her a hug and our silent language sufficed.

Yon, Pia and I walked to school together down a winding and steep-ish street. It was twenty minutes worth of calming clarity as I began to understand the legitimacy of the school. We could not escape the pervasive aroma of fermented corn flower with an ever-so-mild hint of ammonia in the air coming from the tortilleria we passed on the opposite side of the street. The smell was evocative of walking past the Dietz & Watson lunch meat factory in Philly and made me feel that I had simply been transported to another neighborhood, just with different people and different plants. As we walked, I learned that Yon and Pia, boyfriend and girlfriend, were in Cuernavaca for an entire semester. They were a few years younger than me and finishing up their graduate studies through an exchange program offered by their university in Norway. I also discovered that Pia and I had the same birthday.

When we arrived, Yon and Pia delivered me to the central office where the staff spoke to me in English this one time to orient me to the school and review my itinerary. A peace and love throwback dude named Angel, who could easily be one of the human characters on *Sesame Street*, seemed to be in charge. Angel had a 1970s-esque coolness about him. He escorted me through the back door of the office into an exotic, landscaped botanical garden that surrounded an in-ground swimming pool. The "classrooms" consisted of about ten sets of patio tables and chairs adorning the perimeter of the pool, each with their own easel chalkboard.

Despite the casual, relaxed setting, the teachers took their responsibility very seriously. It was an immersion program, so students were only permitted to speak their native languages in class during the first week, and even that was limited to necessity. Likewise, host families were forbidden to speak to students in anything but Spanish, if they even could. As somewhat of an ethnocentric American back then, I was really surprised to find that most people in Cuernavaca did not speak a word of English. And, I was singly American among my schoolmates. Curiously, most of the students were from Europe. But English is ubiquitously spoken in Europe, especially among contemporary college students. *Thank goodness!*

Later that afternoon, a short, robust woman with cropped, wavy auburn hair who could have passed for an Italian met me at the school. She was the mother of my host family, Señora Lucia, and walked me several blocks up a hill away from the school and around a bend to her home, all the way with my luggage in tow. She adamantly insisted on pulling my suitcases herself in a not-so-silent communication in Spanish. This new place would be my home for the next four weeks. Talk about a healing experience! I didn't have an ounce of adrenaline to spare fretting about Evan.

Cuernavaca is known as the City of Eternal Spring for its gorgeous and consistent weather—the average daily temperature hovers around 78-80°F. It is also known for the large numbers of visiting students who travel there to study the Spanish language. Apparently, the Norwegians living 5,700 miles away knew this, as did their European neighbors who made up my classmates: the Swedes, Finns, Swiss and an Italian girl! I, naturally, sharing a continent with the school, knew none of this.

Though I escaped an allergic reaction to Nadia's cats, I was certainly ill prepared for the mosquitoes that shared our outdoor classrooms. After my first few days of classes, my legs from my shorts line to my ankles were covered in itchy red bumps. Somehow, Señora Lucia imparted directions to me to the farmacia in "el centro"—the downtown section. *How* remains a great wonder of my trip. Spoken directions are difficult for me to remember in my OWN language, much less a foreign one. No doubt, silent context clues aided the exchange.

Though unsure of my course, the walk into town was transporting. The ancient streets were garlanded with storefronts and office buildings reflecting the convergence of two major historical and cultural influences: Aztec royalty and Spanish colonists. There were archways, wrought iron gates, courtyards, gardens, crucifixes, woodcarvings, oak beams, and adobes. Other than the rifle-armed police, it was a downtown like any other city with banks and coffee shops and outdoor cafes and offices. I got my insect "repelente" and headed back "home."

One of Cuernavaca's biggest surprises for me was its metropolitan personality. Before my trip, I had traveled to beach resorts in Mexico like Acapulco, Cancun, and Cozumel, and had taken excursions to Mayan settlements in the Yucatán peninsula. From movies, I had seen images of sketchy Mexican towns along our common borders. But, I had no prior concept of the thriving town of Cuernavaca until I got there.

A few days later, the afternoon sun was still very warm when I arrived *home* from school, so I decided to soak it up on a chaise on the marble patio outside. Wearing a tangerine strapless bikini and a pair of headphones attached to my Sony Walkman that blared James Taylor, I was startled by Lupe, Señora Lucia's seventeen-year-old daughter when she nudged my arm.

"Hola, Lupe. Qué pasa?"

"Valí, hay tres muchachos en la puerta para te."

"Three guys are at the door for me?" I asked, bewildered. "Lupe, can you please ask what they want while I put on some clothes?" I requested, in English. There was no time for context clues here.

She understood English but responded to me in Spanish: "They said you made plans with each of them to do something this afternoon."

"I did?" *Oh my God*, I thought to myself, *I have no idea what I'm saying to these people! I had better just shut the "f" up.*

"It's very funny because they are all three friends," Lupe chuckled.

I pushed my head through the neck opening of my short-sleeved, black gauze beach dress and slipped into my flip-flops, looking a bit panicked.

"Vamos a la puerta juntos," she instructed.

We walked over to the home's bright orange wrought iron front gate. I smiled and waved at the three amigos who were standing on the other side of the gate laughing back, not at me but at the cuteness of the situation. They got a big kick out of the miscommunication. Angel, Jorge, and Rafael invited me to attend a party at Angel's house that evening. Jorge stepped forward and offered to pick me up and escort me there, to which I accepted. Then they turned to Lupe, and in Spanish told her the details about this party.

"Lupe," I checked, "do you think it's okay for me to go?" I really didn't need permission, but I wanted her blessing.

She nodded "yes." She knew their families well.

Jorge arrived around 7 p.m. He was exhibiting a familiar musky scent—something like an over-the-counter type of cologne you can buy at CVS. Maybe Old Spice, which I recognized from Uncle Frank. It smelled fresher on Jorge and not like that of an older man. He spoke to me in English, and asked me to keep that under wraps. I was only too happy to comply. In fairness, he often tried to teach me Spanish phrases during our conversations.

On our ten-minute drive to the party, I learned that Jorge was actually trilingual—he spoke fluent Japanese! When he was not helping his family with student-hosting duties, he worked for a Japanese silver importer. A few weeks later, I'd travel by bus with the Norwegians on a three-hour excursion to the oldest silver mining town in the Americas, the historic Taxco, and when I saw the presence of various international importers there, it all made sense.

When we arrived at the modest cinder block home of Angel and his lovely wife Maria, there were at least forty people already there including other students and teachers drinking and dancing together on the adobe tile floor. It was so festive and fun. The music was upbeat and all-encompassing. The contemporary, club-like Spanish dance music summoned you to dance. I took a quick survey of the room and was thrilled when my eyes caught a glimpse of Nadia on the makeshift dance floor! I immediately ran over, and we hugged like old friends. Nadia took me by the hand into the kitchen area, introduced me to Maria (in Spanish, of course), and grabbed me a beer and a lime.

As I turned back toward the dancing party guests, Jorge, my chaperone, was standing right there. His protective nature was attractive. I would have never guessed when he first dropped me off at Nadia's home that the two were old family friends, or that he and I would become fast friends. It felt as though the entire town knew each other. A few minutes later, Yon and Pia spotted me and waved me over to them excitedly. The entire crowd began chanting along with the song playing in what sounded like "Berrrgo" (with rolled "r's") "Berrrgo! Berrrgo!" Pia grabbed my arm and pulled me onto the dance floor, and we blended with the knee-bouncing crowd to the music, hands swaying in the air. She and Yon yelled over the music, "Happy Birthday, Virgo!" in their sing-song-y accent. Stunned, I had lost all concept of the calendar dates since arriving in Cuernavaca with the overwhelming disorientation and frenzied experience of it all. I had completely forgotten it was my birthday. Turns out, it was not just my birthday *and* Pia's, but three other students were celebrating theirs that week, as well, which was the impetus for throwing the party.

After the song was over, Yon excused himself for a moment and reappeared holding a bouquet of flowers he and Pia had purchased for me. To say that I was touched is an understatement. I simply could not believe they thought to buy me a birthday present from a coincidental tidbit we exchanged within the first hour of meeting each other. I teared up and stood on my tippy toes to hug the tall couple. Jorge smiled approvingly. He hardly knew me and yet he seemed to be in on it. I wasn't alone on my birthday, after all. As it turned out, I was surrounded by people I felt I had known for eternity, and I was having the time of my life.

I must admit, four weeks is insufficient to become fluent in a language, much less when spending every night in a club or at a party. What I did absorb innately was the magical, ancient, colorful, unassuming and appreciative subculture of Cuernavaca.

Organically, I was aligned with Jorge. We were an unspoken pair—another silent language. There was an informality between us. After all, I had known him the longest of anyone in Cuernavaca...about ten days. And, I had spent all but one of those ten days—the day I traveled to Taxco with my schoolmates—with Jorge in one capacity or another, bumping into him at school, hanging out at the nightclubs and restaurants, etc. I found myself missing him in Taxco.

A week later, my three amigos (Jorge, Raf and Angel) invited me to join them on a trip to a nearby lake. I had hoped another female student, the girl from Italy, would join us. When we arrived at the house where she was staying, no one was home. So, the three of us journeyed an hour or so further south to a lake resort called Tequesquitengo, frequented by locals. It was strange to see roadside directional signs for Acapulco along the way, which was another hour and a half due south of Tequesquitengo. When we arrived, the guys ordered margaritas and appetizers. It reminded me of a miniature Lake Tahoe resort. I had no idea that we were going to water ski on the lake! It was only my second time water skiing in my life. Angel commandeered a boat, and I was able to get up on the skis for a good twenty-minute ride on the placid lake water. The sun was hot. I could feel the glow my cheeks had acquired and the tightening of my skin from the lake water.

On the drive back to Cuernavaca, we stopped for dinner at a roadside eatery. The guys raved about the pork at this place. Stepping inside was like stepping back in time. For one thing, Coca-Colas were served in green glass bottles reminiscent of the 1950s, as was the diner itself with swiveling stationary stools around a Formica countertop and few scattered wooden tables and chairs. Unlike the diners of America's "happy days," this place was inside of the owner's home. It was actually one big room—half diner on one side, and half living room on the other, with no divider. Not even a curtain separated the two areas.

The heavy-set, dismal-looking woman got right to work cooking for us behind the counter, with very little conversation exchanged between the guys and her. It was weirdly quiet, like a classroom during an exam. My companions swapped a little chit-chat with the man (her husband, I assumed), who sat devoid of emotion and expressionless on a beat-up recliner watching a black-and-white portable TV with rabbit ears atop. It seemed clear to me that the cook wasn't too happy about me being there, as she refused to give me eye contact or exchange a smile. *Maybe she thinks the guys picked up one of those "whorey" Americans.*

Finally, the homemade meal—and I mean scratch made in front of us—was ready. The woman served us thinly sliced, white steaming pork on Styrofoam plates surrounded by some yellow rice, roasted chilies and runny refried beans. It was all very delicious. My mouth was on fire and the Coke just wasn't cutting the heat. Rafael suggested a few more cervezas to do the trick.

As we pulled away, sleepy from the sun and beers, daylight was fading behind the dusty shack in the rearview mirror. I fell asleep safely and comfortably resting on Jorge's chest with his right arm around my shoulders in the middle row of Angel's van, so very far away from the Tavern.

B.J. For Real

Soon enough, but lightyears away, I was back at the Tavern changed forever by my retreat to Mexico, which might as well have been a dream. My restaurant experiences in Cuernavaca were steeped with moment-by-moment interactions that created freeze-frame imprints on my memory. I suppose most meals at restaurants are festive, but we tend to take them for granted. I now had a heightened awareness about all of mine—from the citrus remnants of a squeeze of fresh lime on my tortilla, to laughing at a joke through language barriers, to certain music beats that were more indelible than usual.

Remarkably, it was rather easy to slip back into the Tavern's culture. Just walking through the kitchen door seeing Jonesy checking his lottery tickets and the smell of sautéing garlic was all it took. In Philadelphia, where many establishments were closed on Mondays, the Tavern was open and entertained people in town for business, sporting events and concerts, as well as a handful of our regulars. It was business as usual, but Monday nights were slower paced, allowing us to spend more time chatting with patrons and each other, and it wasn't backbreaking. Additionally, we had a great work crew that included my posse of Dana, Rachael, Chrissy, Melanie, Francesca and John Travolta Jerry. A few other girls worked Monday nights, too, like Colleen, Gypsy,

Elise, and a young single mom named Becca, who had a southern twang and was strikingly attractive. Somehow, Becca inexplicably arrived at the Tavern.

Becca was a petite little thing—maybe 5' even. She had short, natural blonde hair that framed her face, big blue eyes, a square chin and an easy smile. She was a cross between Courteney Cox and Sharon Stone. Funny how I remember her stories so well, but I had forgotten all about sharing mine—namely, my Billy Joel skirtings as we hung out in the storage room waiting for our stations to be seated.

Becca had a curious past, to me, anyway. She was from a small town in Central Georgia and minimally mentioned being raised by her estranged great aunt. Though she never said this per se, I got the impression her aunt was odd and Becca's upbringing was lonely, spent mostly in a small bedroom with peeling wallpaper and deafening silence where she passed time imagining a different life. I wasn't clear on how she ended up in Philly. And she was really funny! I remember cackling as she recounted her childhood stories about her town. They were always about someone in the town who had gone missing, like the outed gay son of a minister, or the lady who cheated on her husband with the minister. In her combination Philadelphia-Macon accent, she detailed how the townspeople would whisper about bodies ending up in the bottom of some pond. These yarns weren't too dissimilar from mob folklore I had heard growing up in South Philly.

Sometimes, Melanie would ask Becca questions about the characters with genuine interest as if the stories were undoubtedly nonfiction.

"I don't understand. Did the minister's mistress know his son was gay?" quizzed Mel.

There were some holes in Becca's plots, but it didn't matter because they were amusing. I really liked her. In a way, I felt sad for her. She seemed so alone raising her ten-year-old son. With a questionable past, no future plans, and no living relatives to speak of, her life was a complete departure from my upbringing.

A few years after working at the Tavern, Becca moved to New York to pursue an acting career. Her ticket there was a makeshift lesbian relationship with a blue-blooded trust fund baby she met through Elise. About a year after that, Elaina, August and I were in Manhattan and met up with Becca for dinner in the Village. She was as funny as ever and bursting at the seams to share some BIG news with me.

During a horrific recent Nor'easter, Becca and her partner had been snowed in the Hamptons. They decided to make the best of the bad weather by trudging through the elements to a local restaurant for dinner. And who else was making the best of it that night? Billy Joel. *Just when I thought I was over him!*

Naturally, Becca, her partner, Billy, and his manager, being the only four people in the restaurant, began chatting and eventually ended up at the bar having drinks together. As Becca put it, marinara recipes, punch lines, and have-you-been-there's were traded between the foursome when she finally saw a window of opportunity to mention me, and my near encounters with B.J.

I was so taken that she thought to bring me up in her conversation. We had hardly been in touch during that year, and at best, we were only work acquaintances who rarely socialized outside of the restaurant. Surprisingly, she remembered my stories when I thought no one was paying attention. I mean, my silly fantasies paled in comparison to the real-life adventures Dana was having.

I sat riveted as Becca recounted her conversation with Billy:

"Billy," she addressed him as if sitting on his patio with a champagne in hand, "I would be remiss if I didn't mention I know one of your biggest fans, a friend of mine from Philadelphia. Her name is Valerie. She's a fox. Val has all these funny stories about times when she *almost* got to meet you. She's one of the smartest and funniest women I know. Italian, too."

"Thanks, Becca!" I beamed. I had no idea she saw me that way.

She continued, "I once asked Val what she would say to you if she ever actually got to meet you."

Leaning over his White Russian, Billy Joel, acting interested, asked, "And what was that?"

"Dang it," Becca said, "I can't think of the song title now. She wanted to ask you if a certain song was about sexual abuse. I think it may have been on *The Bridge* album, but it wasn't big on the radio. My apologies; I just don't have the retention."

Billy interrupted, "'Code of Silence'?"

Becca sprang up, "That's it!"

As she recounted her story, I think I stopped breathing for a minute.

"Tell your friend she struck a nerve," said the prolific songster. "Better yet, give me a piece of paper. I want to write her a note."

Becca thought quickly and grabbed the beverage napkin from beneath her glass of syrah. She handed it to Billy. "Will this work?"

Becca reached inside her purse and produced the napkin, then handed it to me across the table. Elaina's and August's mouths dropped almost in unison. I was beside myself. It took me a good minute to process before I read the note aloud:

> To Valerie—
> Ok, already, so where the hell were you?
> We waited & waited—
> But you never showed up!
> Anyway, I missed you again. Dammit!
> Love, Billy Joel

"Flip it over," Becca instructed. There on the back, Billy wrote his "super secret, private, unpublished" phone number.

When I returned home to Philly and reread the note, repeatedly, I knew I had just one chance—ONE—to nail this. My strategy: I began practicing a message I would leave on Billy's voicemail. I wrote a few variations in my notebook and recited them into my Sony cassette recorder.

I don't know why I thought I'd reach his voicemail versus a live person. It never occurred to me that someone might actually answer the phone. In my mind, I had to be pithy, intriguing, sexy and funny—and all in less than a minute's time. This was different than walking him to his hypothetical table that afternoon at the Tavern where he'd get to see me in the 3D. Now, I would be relegated to voice only, and with a South Philly accent at that. I was comforted by reminding myself of *his* accent—a total *New Yawka*.

Once again, grounded, focused, and logical me...was ridiculously out of control. It had gotten to the point that even my dad felt he needed to sit me down and talk some sense into me.

"Val," he warned, "dating a celebrity looks glamorous but it's really not an easy life. They're on the road a lot and there is a lot of infidelity. That's just the nature of the business."

It is hysterical to me now how even my dad thought I had a legitimate chance with Billy Joel. Apparently, the people in my life saw me very differently than I saw myself back then.

I finally brought up the nerve to make the call. And to my great surprise, someone answered the phone. *Uh oh!* I had not planned nor practiced for this.

"Hello. Can I speak to Billy please?" I uttered, sounding more like the receptionist at my doctor's office than a minx.

In a very effeminate voice, the male on the other end of the line quipped abruptly, as though I interrupted him in the middle of watching *Oprah*, "Not here. Did you want to leave a message?"

"Yes. My name is Valerie, I mean Val, I mean he'll probably know me as Valley. Anyway, he sent me a note through our mutual friend Becca with this number and asked me to give him a call. Please tell him he can reach me on my very public and published number, 215-334..."

Ugh! Kill me now. What kind of strategist am I? I blew it!

"Will do," the voice responded. *Click.*

I never heard back.

The entire incident took so much out of me that I never again attempted to call the number. To this day, I cannot believe I allowed myself to get wrapped up in any kind of fantasy. For a very long time afterward, I couldn't even talk about it or listen to his music.

The next time I'd share my wafts with B.J., or attempt to, was several years after leaving the Tavern on a first date with a guy who would one day become my husband. I began my story with enthusiasm; I thought it made for great conversation. But before I got too far into it, he interrupted, "Ugh. I hate Billy Joel's music." And in an instant, my Billy Joel era had ended. Sharing an experience is only as good as the audience you share it with.

Realizing I was probably not going to meet and marry a celebrity, I decided it would be wiser to gamble on my daytime gig and concentrate on my marketing career. Of course, this would mean weaning myself from my shifts and other perks at the Tavern and the cold cash I always enjoyed having in my *real* Fendi wallet.

Phyllis

For at least the first half of my career at the Tavern, I was completely intimidated by Phyllis, the general manager. Phyllis governed with power and threat. Every server knew that one slip-up could banish you in disgrace to the worst two-table station in the house. Slip-ups included customer complaints, admonishment by Jonesy, an inability to accessorize properly, serving the wrong bottle of wine or food, and failure to treat Phyllis and the office staff like paying customers when they came down to the dining room for lunch during the rush...of paying customers. And you never, ever complained about your station. She was brutal and knew just how to administer punishment where it hurt the most: in our Abe-supplied pocketbooks.

Before the days of restaurant computer systems, food orders were placed and checks were added by hand. Hard to believe now. And like anything else involving cash, this left room for human error and temptation.

Each quarter, Phyllis would display a "mistakes" list in the kitchen. If you were on it, you might as well have had to wear a scarlet "$" on your chest for weeks to come. It was written in red Sharpie marker on an 11x17" poster, mounted dead center above the coffee station for all the staff to see. The sage cooks who worked the hot and cold food lines—some of whom had rotted teeth and barely got through high school—used our mistakes to make judgments about our ability to wait tables. They attached stigmas that, in some cases, followed servers throughout their entire careers at the Tavern. It was public humiliation, besides being technically illegal.

Apparently, restaurants had insurance to cover such losses, or at the very least, used them as tax write-offs. This was the consensus among the girls and the subject of our conspiracy theories during pre-shift dinner conversations. It was double dipping! But no one dared to accuse management. Instead, we paid up in cash only. Rumor had it that our mistake money funded Phyllis's shoe collection. Every time I admired a pair of her Louboutins, I'd think of poor Melanie who somehow forgot to charge the Steins for a bottle of Vino Nobile.

When the restaurant finally switched to computers, we got retribution. It was mistake-proof so that meant we no longer had to suffer the disgrace, pay up, or wallow in the fact that Phyllis was wearing our tips.

I steered clear of her for many years for fear of suffering her wrath. But inside, I wouldn't have minded being her friend. If one ever got to be under her wing, it was a good place to be. For one thing, she knew fashion and the best of everything, and she was immensely generous to her friends.

Phyllis had had a humble upbringing but managed to do very well in investments and relationships, though I'm not sure they weren't one in the same for Phyllis—she exclusively dated men of means. Strategy trumped passion for her and her men had to be able to provide Phyllis with a rich and famous lifestyle. She often vacationed in Malibu or Cabo and easily assimilated into those cultures. Phyllis was also a most gracious host whenever she invited you somewhere, and had a special fondness and bigheartedness for little children, although she had none of her own. When the subject of an Ivy League school surfaced with her non-Tavern friends, she could quickly pivot to her husband's children.

A few months after returning from Mexico, a big guy named Doug came into the restaurant for lunch one afternoon. He was 6'2", handsome, and imposing with azure blue eyes and dirty-blond hair, a few years older than me and I didn't know his face, but he seemed to belong there. The next day, a huge vase containing two dozen multicolored roses was delivered to the Tavern for me with no card attached. It took me a week or so to unravel the mystery with help from Phyllis, which led to an eventual date with Doug a few weeks later. We went to the Four Seasons for drinks and hit it off when I realized he was no dummy. I am a sucker for intellectual stimulation and learned that Doug and I shared many of the same favorite books.

Though I didn't know it, I was on my way to carving a spot for myself under Phyllis's wing. Turns out, Doug was a business associate of Phyllis's ex-boyfriend-turned-best-friend, Jake. I was in.

Her first order of business was to take me by limo to New York City and outfit me on Doug's tab. This was her way of looking out for me and showing me the ropes. We had a blast in New York, and I experienced the other side of Phyllis. We went to lots of stores that day and ended up picking out a suit from Henri Bendel on sale for $1,950.00. *Gasp*. Aside from the suede suit gifted to me by Abe after his big win at Bally's Park Place, it was the most expensive item hanging in my closet for years until a wedding dress hung there. Doug paid Phyllis for the suit and I wore it out to dinner with him at Ruth's Chris Steak House.

Prior to the Tavern, the most expensive gifts I had ever received in my life were a 14-karat gold necklace and an Italian-made charm bracelet given to me by Aunt Angela one birthday and Christmas. As a young girl, I had not been accustomed to receiving AT ALL! Yet, it was becoming more comfortable. I could hear the shift acknowledged in the skepticism in August's and Elaina's voices when I'd recount these stories to them. The Tavern was full of extravagance and I was starting to realize that I was sort of in an elite class of women who worked there, entitled to the perks that came with it.

Doug and I were dating for about two months when I began to realize something wasn't kosher about his business, especially when a truckload of boxes full of T-shirts were delivered to my place. Doug called to alert me and asked if he could keep the boxes there for a bit. I wondered why they weren't delivered to his warehouse. Then, I learned why I had never seen Doug in the restaurant before.

It was Francesca who got the scoop. She was friendly with Jake's daughter who reported that Doug had been away for awhile, as in jail. For fraud. Phyllis never breathed a word of this to me. She was of a generation that upheld omertà and I'm sure she figured I'd find out on my own.

By the time I found out, our courtship was already ending. It wasn't only the T-shirts covering an entire wall of my apartment, but our dates went from Le Bec-Fin to LongHorn Steakhouse, and the intellectual conversations were pretty much left at the Four Seasons.

It didn't take long before I heard that Doug lied his way back to the big house. He was finally nabbed impersonating an ophthalmologist and cashing in a $150,000 marker at

Caesars Palace in Atlantic City. He had masterminded a terrific scheme posing as a referral service for doctors. Of course, this was when people still trusted service calls and before the Internet. Hard to believe there was anything before the Internet. He'd call doctors' offices and charm receptionists into providing their bank account information for "annual audit approvals," then use the information to get markers at the casinos. He gambled some of it back to look legit before calling it a night and retiring to a comped suite with room service lobster dinners.

Learning this made me a little sick. I actually considered returning the Henri Bendel suit—I had only worn it once—and using the money for something useful like paying down my student loans. But truthfully, I liked having it hanging in my closet. I walked away with a few other consolation prizes, including a 14-karat white and yellow gold Ebel watch and a five-strand Biwa pearl choker from Tiffany. At that point, I could hear my grandmother Mary's words of wisdom as clear as any living voice:

"Careful. When you lie down with dogs, you get up with fleas."

I know this much: given enough time in any environment, we adapt like chameleons. The Tavern sure had a way of raising the standard of expectations and putting a convincing spin on justification. I was undoubtedly, yet slowly becoming indoctrinated into the lifestyle.

In the end, the best gift of my relationship with Doug was the beginning of a friendship with Phyllis.

Stray Cats and Sly Foxes

An unknown customer approached Rachael for the third time and said sternly, "Look here. We've been waiting an hour. When will my table be ready? My wife is pregnant." It was another jam-packed Saturday night.

"Sir, don't you know that you're supposed to have a sandwich or late afternoon snack before coming to the Tavern for dinner, ESPECIALLY if your wife is pregnant?" Rachael delivered while never once breaking her most sincere smile. Her sarcasm was so well hidden behind her seemingly happy face. "Now, if you'll go back to the bar, I'll call you as soon as the table is ready," she finished and turned to pick up an incoming phone call. Dumbfounded, the customer returned to his seat and waited for his table. She was a master.

He could have played it differently. If he had approached Rachael with so much or so little, relatively speaking, as a $20 bill in his hand, her response may have been more like this: "I'm so sorry, sir. I know it's a long wait tonight. I'd offer your wife some bread, but we're not allowed to serve food at the bar. Look, I'll put a little star next to your name here on my waiting list to remind me of your wife's condition, and I'll let you know as soon as your table is ready." He would still have waited over an hour. I mean, he wasn't a regular and he would have had to up the ante for a sincere effort on Rachael's part. But, at least he would have returned to the bar with a sense of accomplishment and some fodder for chest beating.

It was a give and take there. The customers worked us, so to speak, and we worked them.

Ivy cajoled her customers with sophistication and intellect, often discussing her ex-husband's sculptures. Her ex, Tristin, was a native of France and Ivy was a girl from Northeast Philly who could roll the Yiddish off her tongue when needed. Tristin's eyes were opened to creating the most beautiful stone and marble art that captured Ivy's heart initially. Otherwise, they were darkened by a pair of chauvinistic shades. Ivy sometimes referred to him as a "cave dweller." Ironically, his carvings made great tableside conversation.

Valentina, a young single mom, wore her son's picture in a large locket around her neck with the off chance of evoking pity in the form of healthy tips. Chrissy worked the rescue pet angle.

Trina, a part-time hostess, would lean in and nonchalantly rub her breasts against men sitting at the bar. The wives hated her and could smell her motives and plasticity the minute they walked in the door. Some complained to the office about the behavior. Instead of being reprimanded—or fired—Phyllis told her to curtail the back rubs to weeknights.

Many of the Tavern girls patronized the customers, flirting on weeknights and fawning over the wives of regulars on the weekends. But no one there extended themselves quite like Shelly, a woman who held two positions at the Tavern as both a hostess and a server. She worked every shift when the place was open. Living well beyond her means, Shelly was imprisoned by debt. Her desperation manifested in many money-making tricks up her sleeveless and revealing royal blue leather dress. But not the kind you'd think. Put another way, she was an ice queen.

Shelly was a petite girl with big, blue eyes and sassy, shiny black hair in a pixie cut. She was built and dressed like a fashion doll with no hips and deep cleavage. She was from Long Island, N.Y., had a Broadway voice, and a real talent for interior design. Unlike the rest of us, she was not interested in being wined and dined. More inviting to her would have been a discounted interest rate on her BMW lease.

Shelly invented dishes not on the menu. Whenever someone ordered any cut of meat, she'd ask if they wanted it topped with lump crabmeat or grilled shrimp, as if to imply the dish came with one of these options. These options added another $15 to each entree. Very rarely did affected Tavern regulars question a bill. Like a used car salesman, Shelly could have convinced a diabetic to order a chocolate mousse. "It's not that sweet, really."

One summer weeknight, a morbidly obese man came into the restaurant alone and sat in her station. Her eyes widened with possibilities. Ivy was standing by the podium when he walked in. She leaned into Rachael and said under her breath, "Here comes Shelly's next mortgage payment." Shelly sold the big man a langoustine appetizer for two, and TWO of the largest entrees on the menu: twin lobster tails (14 oz. each) and the 3 lb. double veal chop. He left with a doggie bag.

Her suburban townhouse looked like a center spread in *Better Homes and Gardens*. I was at Shelly's once when she hosted a graduation party for Chrissy for completing her Master of Acupuncture program. (We surmised the *real* reason for the party was to show off a baby grand piano.)

The house was so perfect, we were afraid to eat and drop a crumb, as well as being a little afraid of *what* we were eating. Shelly was an excellent cook and baker, too, although we seemed to find cat hairs on everything she ever brought to work for us to sample. We later figured out that her cat used to hang out on a dish towel on her kitchen counter, which was probably never introduced to her washing machine. Don't get me wrong; Shelly wasn't a dirty person. But washing the dish towel just wasn't a priority for a girl who worked eighty-five hours a week. The point being, she had so much talent and she spent every waking moment at the Tavern. For Shelly it was a vicious cycle.

Her check averages were routinely higher than anyone else's, especially after a big purchase was made like the piano for her living room. But that only upped the pressure to earn more, and spillover of her obsession inevitably affected her co-workers.

For every capacity Shelly possessed, there was an equal and opposite incapacity. If a "nobody" sat too long after paying the check, she'd stalk them with hostile folded arms until they got the hint and got out. Since reservations were not taken on Saturday nights, it was first come, first served and the pressure to turn tables was even greater. With Shelly at the hostess helm, servers knew we'd better turn our tables quickly...or else she would ensure the best tippers were seated in someone else's station for the rest of the night. Ultimately, she made great bribe money from regulars by bumping them ahead of waiting customers. The heavy hitters would slip her a $50 bill or a Benjamin and expected to sit at a table when and where they wanted. It was all about the churn.

Once, shortly after the untimely passing of one of Ivy's

best friends, Ivy was back at work on a typical Saturday night waiting on a table that just wouldn't leave. They were talking and laughing long after the check had been paid. *How dare they enjoy themselves beyond their welcome at the priciest restaurant in town?* Shelly was furious because Joe Starsky, the owner of a huge trucking line, had just slipped her a $50 bill and he was hungry.

She walked over to Ivy, who was standing by the table anxiously awaiting the customer to vacate. Shelly got right in front of Ivy's face, like a drill sergeant with a mean scowl, and said, "I don't care who died, turn your tables or the office will find out about this," through a clenched jaw.

Two things resulted. One: overhearing the warning and surprisingly feeling empathy for Ivy, the customers got up and left in an instant. And, two: on her way out that evening, Ivy passed Shelly's fox coat hanging in the coatroom. She made an about face, looking over her shoulders to see if anyone else was around, opened the jacket and blew her nose in the lining.

Shelly was a prime example of wasted potential. You liked her and disliked her. When she entertained at her home, you really liked and admired her because she was a gracious hostess and served generous portions of the best of everything. Additionally, her guard was down and she was proud to show us her home. She even laughed. Sadly, when it came to the Tavern, you often disliked working with her. She was a money-hungry maniac, driven to afford her material world and could be downright nasty. She would hoodwink you out of your turn to wait on a big tipper by sneakily seating them in her own station while you were in the bathroom or kitchen on the nights she waited tables instead of hostessing. She'd physically push another server out of the way to beat you to the last ramekin of tiramisu so she wouldn't have to tell her customers we'd run out. There was that side of Shelly that deserved every ounce of snot Ivy could expel.

No doubt that when Shelly arrived home after midnight that evening, she satisfactorily hung her fox coat on a padded hanger in the foyer closet, unaware of the hardening mucous spot on its silk lining. On her way upstairs, she walked past her state-of-the-art, rear-projection large screen TV covering the better part of the family room wall that she probably only watched once or twice, having spent every day but Sundays at the Tavern to pay for it. I thought about Señora Lucia's entire family in Cuernavaca, gathered around a 13" black-and-white TV, watching a ten-year-old rerun of *Rambo* with English subtitles, genuinely enjoying it and each other. And then I thought about Shelly climbing into her king-size brass bed, with throbbing feet from standing for hours at the hostess podium in her 5" pointy-toed Manolo Blahniks, completely alone. I wanted to shake her into reality, but I know we each have our own paths of evolution.

My Best Breast Forward

B eing intellectually driven, I HATE admitting this, but my breasts opened many doors for me. Hence the moniker given to me by Jonesy that stuck with Tavern staffers, "Big Tit Val," which I accepted lovingly. It was just another South Philly nickname that both described and distinguished you. Truthfully, my chest often preceded me, and sometimes my assets were a liability.

Once, while walking across the dining room holding a tray of coffees, I felt something warm on my right breast. I looked down and saw my boob resting in the foam atop a cappuccino. The milk had formed a circle positioned perfectly over my nipple. *Oh my God! What should I do? Think fast. There's no turning back. Okay, you're here; just make a joke of it.*

"Breast milk cappuccino, anyone?" I suggested as I got to the table. As the eight golf-shirted men before me roared, I knew my quick wit and mild smuttiness increased my tip exponentially. Luckily, it was a weeknight. Even so, there was a certain knack for understanding which clientele could handle that forward humor and who would find it inappropriate. We knew instinctively.

One Wednesday evening at a nearby Italian restaurant where Rachael, Chrissy, Gypsy, Phyllis, Nancy and I met for dinner, we were seated next to a table of older guys we knew loosely from the Tavern. Phyllis, who could be quite a tyrant in her role as general manager at the Tavern, was a fun-seeking, ever-so-generous socialite outside of there, as I mentioned. I had joined the ladies directly from my day job wearing a black Donna Karan suit that did not require a blouse beneath it. The men seated next to us spoke broken English. They were Italian businessmen (from Italy) having dinner after their monthly NIA-PAC (National Italian American Political Action Committee) meetings.

After three bottles of Château Margaux—only the best for Phyllis—she began to initiate this seemingly aimless conversation with the Italians about doing body shots...a "fun" antic for drunken fools whereby a body part is used to serve up a shot of your favorite liquor. *Enter the fool.* One thing led to another and before we knew it, my cleavage became the target of an abridged body shot challenge.

Before I knew it, I was looking down at a dense, kinky crop of salt and pepper hair as one of the Italian men lifted a shot glass of limoncello from the intersection of my bra cups using just his teeth. Sometimes it was difficult to balance my professional life with my Tavern life. I surely didn't want to be a stick in the mud, but I was also responsible for leading the marketing-communications department at an uptown bank, and reporting to a board of directors. For the moment, my double life seemed to be under wraps in the otherwise empty and dimly lit, Art Deco dining room that Wednesday evening. We girls and the Italians were the only patrons there, *thank goodness.* I laughed along with my dinner mates about the acrobatics.

I'm not sure if anyone realized this at the time, and especially after a few rounds of limoncello shots, but Chrissy had captured photos of the charming and classy event with her mini Canon. I'm thankful for my ever-prudent inner voice and the wherewithal that kept my suit jacket on and buttoned, the pictures later revealed.

Fast forward. Six months later, I was at a job interview for a director-level marketing and PR position at an even larger uptown financial institution. Like anyone who prepares for an interview, I was dressed professionally, had my credentials in my briefcase and waited patiently in the lobby to be called into the president's office.

The time finally came. I walked confidently into the spacious, well-appointed suite, put my hand out to shake his, and nearly had a heart attack. *Holy Jesus! Could this be possible?* He was one of the Italians at the body shots dinner. *Quick! Regain yourself. Deny, deny, deny. At least he's not the one who did the shot. Maybe he won't remember you.*

"Thank you for this opportunity," I said quickly.

As the interview progressed, I had a gut feeling he recognized me. I was dying to say something and finally got the nerve up. "You look familiar to me. Have we met before?"

The bank president responded decisively and defensively. "No, we've never met before."

Whew! I'm with you, man! It was obvious he was just as uncomfortable with the event as I was. We both preferred to pretend it never happened. Choosing the path of denial spared my embarrassment and allowed us to move on for the sake of the interview. Those Tavern girls and their bad influence on me! *Be quiet, Grandmom Mary!* I sternly told the voice in my head. *I know! I know! "Lie down with dogs and you get up with fleas."*

That's not to say that my beloved Tavern cohorts were the dogs in the body shots scenario. Dirty sometimes? Yes.

Female dogs (as in *bitches*) sometimes? Yes. But also fucking fun, worldly, sharp and kind. Solid friends who I can still call today, even in the middle of the night if I need to.

Outside of the thirty-seventh-floor building, when I landed back on firmer ground, I took a deep sigh, then laughed out loud. The top half of my body collapsed at my waist, allowing my hair to fall upside down. *I cannot believe that just happened!* I stood back up and imagined throwing a coin into the air: *Headlights I get the job, tails I don't.*

I got the job. I guess in spite of the body shots debacle, I did have a solid resume and strong bank marketing experience. At least, that's what I told myself. My new boss would never come to know about the photos I acquired from Chrissy, and I would come to prove my abilities and business acumen on the job.

I suppose I have my grandmothers to thank in part for my conscience as well as my endowments. These women sported no less than seven inches of cleavage, and, I might add, a gift that served them well. My father delivered a family favorite story about Grandmom Josie's boobs with the hilarity, body language and timing as only he could.

His cousin, Loretta, was born a month after him in 1935. Loretta's mom, my Great-Aunt Annie, was unable to produce breast milk. As a result, my grandmother nursed both babies alternately: Dad and cousin Loretta. Loretta grew up to be more buxom, and Dad was svelte. So he always joked she got more "swigs," leaving less supply for him. I wish I could convey his side-splittingly funny delivery of this story in writing, but those who experienced it know exactly what I'm talking about.

Grandmom Mary's boobs aren't story-less, either. Once,

when babysitting my older cousin Chuckie as a toddler, and trying to rock him to sleep on her bosom, he bit my grandmother's right breast, landing her in the ER. Good thing Chuckie was a little menace because the incident revealed a tumor requiring immediate surgery.

I wondered how many other untold opportunities my grandmothers' breasts facilitated back then. *What would my grandmothers think of my Tavern nickname?* Even if they weren't fond of the language, I could almost hear them complimenting my Donna Karan shirtless suit. "Oh, that Valerie. She can really wear clothes," Grandmom Josie would say.

No Offense Taken

I heard Ivy beeping the horn outside my house and quickly grabbed *The Artist's Way* workbook, my purse and a banana. I had just gotten home from the bank without time to eat and I didn't want to be late for our first class. At Ivy's suggestion, we enrolled in a twelve-week seminar at the Jewish Arts Center in town on Tuesday evenings, a rather slow dinner shift at the Tavern and our mutual night off from work. The course and the book that inspired its method were developed to harness one's creative talent. I was looking to unblock my ability to write a book, and Ivy to oil paint.

"Hi," I greeted Ivy excitedly as I climbed into her passenger seat. I affixed the seatbelt and immediately began peeling back the perfectly sunshine yellow skin of my banana. "Would you like half of my banana?" I offered. "I had meetings all day at work and I'm starving!"

"No, honey, I'm good. Thanks." Ivy continued without taking a breath, "Hey Valley Girl, would you believe Shelly told Phyllis I spend too much time talking to customers about sculptures and that I don't turn my tables quickly enough, after I've worked at the Tavern for fifteen years?"

"Ugh. That girl needs a life!" I protested. "So, what did Phyllis say?"

"It's back downstairs to section A, *again*," Ivy confessed sarcastically.

"Ah, the old waitress shaming never gets old here," I groused, "and with our collective education, it's so offensive."

"Well, if I'm being honest, it's a closer walk from the kitchen than upstairs for carrying trays. I really don't mind it. Of course, I wouldn't dare let on," she rationalized while checking her rearview mirror.

"God forbid!" I proclaimed. "What, then? Banishment to the coatroom? Wait, I'm sorry, that station has already been taken by Stephie." We shared a unison chuckle. "Would you believe I'm approaching *nine* years there?" I switched gears. "Oh, and speaking of Shelly, I have a funny story for you."

Ivy and I rarely missed a beat in conversations. We could banter seamlessly from one topic to the next without transition sentences and follow each other just fine.

I dove right into my gossip. "Last night in the kitchen, Dom Scarpinato called me over to the hot line and proceeded to break a story like he was giving me a tip on a horse."

"Hey Val," Scarpy began out of the side of his mouth while sautéing chicken piccata. "Did you hear that crumb-bum, Shelly, doesn't use women's sanitary products when she has her thing?" he confided.

Ivy interjected the story as she braked for a red light, thinking she misheard something. "Wait a minute...*what*?"

Through my chortling it was hard to finish, but I continued. "He went on to say that she works every Goddamn day the place is open and makes more money than Micky but is too cheap to pay for sanitary products."

"And, what did you possibly respond to him?" Ivy asked half shocked, half not—*nothing would surprise us about anyone there*—while she navigated rush-hour traffic on Broad Street.

I screeched, "WHAT, Scarpy! That's ridiculous! Where

the hell did you hear that?"

"Deaf Eddie told me," he answered straight-faced, and tossed a handful of capers into the sauté pan.

Ivy was cackling and nearly sideswiped another car trying to switch lanes. She slapped the steering wheel with her right hand and snorted, "I can't wait to hear the rest."

"I'm not sure why I bothered with an attempt at reasonability but I said, 'Scarpy, how in the world would Eddie know that? We don't call him *Deaf* Eddie for nothing!'"

Scarp shot back, "I know, I'm not fucking stupid! Eddie reads lips. He overheard her telling the other girls," he affirmed, flipping the chicken with a lurch of the pan.

"I thought, what a revelation! It's Deaf Eddie who's been fueling the rumor mill! Maybe *he's* the one who told Phyllis you talk too much to your customers?" I finished. Ivy and I howled.

"I mean, we all know that political correctness fails to exist inside the Tavern, but this story is one for the books!" Ivy mused. "The sauté cook tells you about a rumor he heard from the deaf stock guy! I can't even take it."

"Besides that," I added, "could you imagine nicknaming a deaf person 'Deaf' in any other setting and that person being okay with it? Only in South Philly, I swear!" I asserted, shaking my head.

"Wait," Ivy questioned, "How do you know Eddie's not offended?"

"He reads lips!" I boomed. We roared some more.

"Unbelievable, the goings-on in that place, eh?" Ivy conceded. We grabbed our *Artist's Way* workbooks from the back seat of her car. Ivy pressed the auto-lock feature on her key fob as we walked toward the garage elevator.

When I stopped to think about the nature of the conversations I'd shared with the Tavern cooks over the years, and then envisioned the chats with my banking colleagues around the proverbial water cooler, my head tilted back and forth at the juxtaposition, much the same way I straddled the two worlds I occupied.

Ivy looked back at her car once more to be sure the lights had turned off, then turned back toward me. "But do you think it's true about Shelly?" she wondered aloud.

"Who the hell knows. Nothing would surprise me. Do you think Shelly knows you blew your nose in her coat?" I countered.

She shrugged her right shoulder as if to say, "Good point."

"I'll tell you, though, Ivy," I added, switching to a serious tone. "I am tired of waiting tables. I'm really beginning to feel the tension between my corporate life and the Tavern world."

The elevator appeared stuck on the fifth floor. While we waited for it, I continued my lament. "Last Monday night, a few businessmen came in for dinner and sat in my station. We immediately recognized each other because they're reps from a software company who had just pitched me and colleagues at the bank earlier that day. They were shocked to see me in my restaurant capacity. I explained that I started at the Tavern in college and kept it because the extra money is great, it's good exercise, etcetera. You know, all the bullshit."

We stepped into the tiny and empty garage elevator, Ivy pressed the button for the second floor, and I resumed my story. "Truthfully, I was a little embarrassed because it undermines my status and achievements in my career. Although, I must admit, serving professional colleagues dinner and drinks at the Tavern pales in comparison to arriving at an interview, facing my potential future boss, and realizing his buddy used my cleavage as a vessel for taking a shot of limoncello! Know what I'm saying?" I offered my thoughts with self-deprecating sarcasm.

"I can understand what you're saying," Ivy smiled, "but that *was* hilarious! Working with children during the day, I don't have the same encounters you have in business." The always sensible Ivy quickly pivoted, "Can you afford to quit the Tavern?"

"I don't know," I answered with authentic uncertainty. "It will be hard to give up two grand a month. And what the hell would I write about? No more Shelly stories. So, this decision will have to wait at least until after *The Artist's Way* wraps up," I joked.

"Oh, yeah, we can't have that. You definitely need to write these stories down, Valley Girl," Ivy agreed.

It never occurred to me that I would remain at the Tavern after landing my first professional job. After working there for nearly a decade, it had become habitual. As I became more established and entrenched in the career I truly desired, I had increasing awareness that my life was evolving away from the restaurant. I was finally and seriously visualizing my departure from the Tavern. I deliberated about more than just the money, which was pretty compelling alone. *I mean, two grand a month covers rent and utilities.* But when I really thought about it, it also meant giving up connections and shared experiences not only with my co-workers, but with some regular customers, too, who had become part of my social network.

Then again, it was hard to reconcile serving the software reps an antipasto while sporting a server's pouch belted around the same skirt I wore when I shook their hands in the bank boardroom earlier that day...and to be taken seriously. They poked a little fun at me for how well I recited the specials.

"You must have gone to college for that," one of them jested. Ostensibly, I made a reflexive facial expression because he quickly followed up with, "I was just joking. I hope I didn't offend you."

I wished I had responded somewhat sarcastically with, "Yes, as a matter of fact, I'm working on my master's degree." Which was true. Instead, I lied. "No offense taken," I replied with a (fake) smile.

B.J. of a Different Sort

The winds of change were underway. The cherry blossoms that lined Willow Street along the scrupulous row of red brick homes were bare. And I, bearing a master's degree, was entering my thirtieth year of life and my eleventh year at the Tavern.

So much had transpired over the previous decade. For one thing, Micky decided to put a few women behind the bar on Monday nights for a change and asked me to be one of them! From day one, bartending was strictly a male profession at the Tavern. Since the arrival of other hot, new restaurants with novelty drinks and trendy appetizers appeared on the scene, Micky felt the need to make some minor tweaks. Monday nights were a safe place to start. Cheryl, "Irish MFer," tended the upstairs bar and I worked downstairs.

Besides that, I had also finished grad school at night, bought a home, worked my way up to a director's position at my day job, traveled to four countries on two continents, gained a few nieces and nephews, lost both my grandmothers—two women who helped frame me—and dated, a lot. It was time to rethink things.

Ever since Evan, I especially had my antenna up when meeting guys who were "GU." That is, "Geographically Undesirable" as Elaina would categorize anyone who lived further than a half-hour drive away. Those thirty-minute restrictions never entered the minds of Tavern girls, who were more focused on a different demographic: socioeconomic status (meaning six- and seven-figure salary baselines). Besides, they found the prospect of whisking away somewhere—even an hour and a half north to New York—adventurous and exciting. I, on the other hand, was a little of both. Any guys who were *too* available didn't appeal to me. I liked my space, and subliminally the exploratory mission of dating that had a built-in escape hatch if needed. At the same time, I was becoming keenly aware of my age and my desire to start a family.

I remembered talking to a therapist I saw a few times at Mel's urging during our "Co-D" rides home from work several years earlier. The woman had asked me, somewhat rhetorically, why I entered relationships spying the exit signs. I was starting to see her point.

When I really thought about it, I could trace my trepidations as far back as a marriage proposal I received from my high school boyfriend inscribed inside of my yearbook cover. I broke into hives and couldn't sleep for two days after reading it. It pushed me far enough to live away at college but kept me close enough to come home on weekends. Back then, the thought of spending the rest of my life in a row home in South Philly was suffocating. Living there now feels entrepreneurial and hip—funny how one's perspective changes.

"How did I become noncommittal?" I proposed to Dr. Peters, my new therapist. "How did I become so noncommittal?" I repeated the question, asking myself more so than him.

His eyes blinked open. "How do you think you became

noncommittal?" *Did he seriously just nod off? Of all the insults to injury! I guess he's heard this story a few times before. Or maybe he didn't get a good night's sleep.* The clock was ticking, and I had no time to analyze him.

"First, you need to ask yourself if 'noncommittal' is an accurate description. From what you've told me, it seems you have been loyal in your relationships," he promptly dove back in, unapologetically, for having dozed off.

"Yes, but I chose partners who were unavailable to me either physically or emotionally." *As if to imply I had outgrown the habit. Ahem.* "Like Evan. In addition to knowing from the start he was going to be moving across the country, he smoked a lot of weed, which made me feel like he wasn't really there at times," I admitted.

"He *wasn't* present. So, why was that okay for you?" Peters challenged.

"It was okay at times, especially when I indulged with him. But the whole relationship caught me by surprise, even though I always knew there was an end in sight. I guess eventually I would have addressed it if it had become a problem. Maybe our chemistry would have been enough to take the good with the bad? Does that make sense?" I reasoned.

"Yes. However, you have said that you stayed in a relationship with your college boyfriend, Alex, for all the wrong reasons. Okay. We have to stop here," he closed. *Ugh! I hate the forty-five minute wrap-up of a one-hour conventional therapy session almost as much as I hate paying for answering my own questions!*

"Think about why you are willing to surrender some of your desires in relationships," Dr. Peters concluded, "and I'll see you next week."

And why aren't you accountable for sleeping on my time?????
I thought. I left the office without actually voicing those
feelings, of course, but felt frustrated. It was back to torturing
August and Elaina for free counseling, I supposed.

But in moments of clarity, I knew the answer to the
question I was asking: fear. Fear of becoming bored with my
partner. Fear of being strangled by routines. Fear of being
unable to maintain my individuality. Fear of codependency.

At this moment, life was standing still temporarily without
much to excite me. Whenever I allowed myself quiet time
between jobs and social activities, waves of depression would
wash over me, then recede again. I couldn't just pick up and
leave the country every time I hit a patch of drabness. On one
hand, I wanted to settle down, but the prospect of prospecting
was uncertain, and I was lacking a bit of energy. I had met a
lot of nice, traditional guys through business during the day,
but they seemed to lack the jet-setting adventure of, say, the
Tavern customers. Having transitioned to only two shifts a
week at the Tavern—one as a bartender and the other as a
server—I kept one foot in the restaurant world and the other
out. Commitment.

Even being invited to one of Louie's soirées no longer
offered a thrill. Watching the usual cast of mostly married
men tell the same stupid jokes and salivate over women
whenever they got a get-out-of-jail-free card from their wives
had gotten old. Nonetheless, with nothing better to do than
watch *Law & Order* one night, I accepted an invitation from
Louie to attend a dinner party at the prominent Matthew's
Steakhouse uptown. At the very least, I figured Tim and
Marvin, two Monday night regulars who sat at the bar and
had become my pals, would be there to make me laugh.

On this particular night, Louie arranged the table seating in boy/girl formation. It was this silly nonsense that made his parties kind of fun. Besides, they were lavish, Romanesque banquets with no fewer than fifty guests and courses of crabmeat-topped dishes, tender filet mignons and the best wines.

Of late, there had been a few new female guests at the dinners who appeared to be like Tavern girls—fun-loving. But upon closer inspection, we figured out these girls were hired and interspersed among the partygoers to take care of indulgent men in a private room, or a bathroom, depending on where the dinner was held. They were strippers Louie met in Key West and began flying them to Philly for his parties. I felt sadness for these girls, and disappointment in my friend, Louie. They were treated kindly, for the most part. Yet, there came a point, many bottles of Dom Pérignon and Opus One later, when they were treated decidedly different from the rest of us women guests. It was disheartening that Louie's parties had degenerated into this. Sadly, Louie used his unlimited funds to buy justification. "After all," I overheard him say, "those girls made at least a couple of grand each that night."

At the start of this particular party, I had the pleasure of sitting next to a newcomer—a very distinguished-looking gentleman I had never met before. He was about twenty years my senior and impeccably dressed, with a perfectly starched white button-down shirt beneath his tie and custom-made suit. His name was Robert Edward Jamison, or B.J. as his friends and colleagues called him. *Ha!* He had a classic Hollywood leading man look—a fairer-complected Cary Grant with silverish, slicked back hair and gray eyes. And his smell was just as alluring. Carnation, spice and tobacco.

It was Chanel Égoïste, an unmistakable olfactory memory I conjured from a sampling at the perfume counter at Bergdorf Goodman in New York.

B.J. stood out from the crowd in many ways, his height being an obvious one at 6'5". He was conversant and charismatic. As the owner and founder of a prestigious Philadelphia accounting firm, he was also a little guarded with an edge of superiority. His body language said, "Come closer, but not too close. Okay, stop there. On second thought, I want your undivided attention." One would not realize upon meeting him that he had grown up in South Philly, as he had lived most of his adult life on an estate in affluent Bucks County.

Most of the guys at the party were successful businessmen but more casual, and Louie's parties had a way of transforming this gang of mid-lifers into drooling dogs, hoping for a chance to relive their teenage years. B.J. outclassed all of them.

I was different, too. I had become a voyeur among the partygoers versus a participant. My stint of body shots days was distantly behind me, thankfully. My intellectual drivers and professional aspirations made it easier to be an observer of the shenanigans despite the copious alcohol. B.J. invited himself into my personal space. We became so engrossed in organic conversation that we were oblivious to the drooling dogs and Key West entertainment for a few hours. We covered movies and movie trivia, current events, and politics, for which we held the same positions. We talked about the upcoming charitable event I was chairing for the National Cancer Society as a representative for the bank where I worked. B.J. gave me his business card to call on him for financial support for the charity. We talked about growing up downtown and discovered we both had a weird fascination for peeking inconspicuously into the windows of South Philly row homes to see how people utilized the small living spaces. We shared a love of word games. For the first time in a long time, I was talking to a like-minded person, not to mention one with old school charm, and I felt alive.

At one point he asked me to dance. I was thrown back to stories my mom told of going to the weekly church dances when she was a teenager. B.J. was closer to her age than mine. He was stiff and had no rhythmic ability. It made me laugh out loud, though I quickly caught myself to not hurt his feelings. He stepped rigidly from side to side, lifting one foot at a time. It didn't take away from his swagger; I liked that there was something imperfect about him.

While B.J. offered a fresh breath, I wanted to get out of there before the after-dinner drinks were served. Not only did I have to be in my office for a board meeting early the next morning, but the extravagance was played out. B.J. left, too, and waited outside with me for a cab.

He turned to me and said, "Tell me something not many people would know about you."

I hesitate to admit that I was nearly sold by that question alone. It was like dating trivia!

"Okay. Let me think for a minute… Oh, here's something. I once had a dog I was so connected to, and I believe she astral traveled to me while I was away in Mexico. How about you?"

"I'm sorry I asked," he quipped with sarcasm honed perfectly by South Philadelphians, and we both laughed. "Okay, my turn. I have a system for choosing my suits and ties in the morning."

"Huh?"

"Each morning I multiply the date by five, for five workdays in a week. I take the last two digits of the answer and that determines which tie I'll wear. I count my ties until I arrive at the two-digit number," he explained.

"Sorry *I* asked."

"Touché," he retorted with a smile.

"Oh God! Wait a minute! Are you a Virgo?"

"Yes," he answered with a puzzled look on his face. "Why do you ask?"

"I know those quirks too well."

"I don't pay much attention to horoscopes. Oh—here's your taxi!"

"Well, thanks for waiting with me. It was fun."

"Will I see you again?" he wondered.

"Yes. I'll give you a call. You know, about the fundraiser."

Inside this mid-fifties, incredibly accomplished CEO businessman was a wide-eyed boy eager to embrace a relationship as if for the first time. On the way home in the taxi, I smiled about the corniness of it. I mean really, "*What's your sign?*"

I called him a few weeks later. We met for dinner at the Ritz-Carlton. We talked easily. I was pleasantly surprised by his reserved approach, considering that I had become accustomed to the advances of Tavern regulars, or even guys I dated of a younger generation who had fewer rules of engagement. I was relieved when I realized I could enjoy him without the threat of him trying to get into my pants. Although he was handsome, I was uncertain about dating an older man or if I'd be attracted to him in undressed ways. (Age would later become a moot point.) Plus, I already understood that B.J. had raised a family and had zero interest in having another one.

A few months had gone by. B.J. attended my National Cancer Society event, and his company made a $5,000 donation. (When Louie found out, he donated $10,000.) B.J. and I spent a lot of time at dinners and lunches getting to know each other as friends and we talked on the phone with greater frequency until we spoke every day, then twice a day. With each conversation, I honed a deeper understanding of him. In so many ways, he was the male me and met me exactly where I was at mentally. We could be silly with each other, too, like playing word games on drink napkins at restaurants. He was quite good at creating cryptograms. I loved his quick mind. He was well rounded, self-assured and had just enough South Philly cockiness to give him edge.

Naturally, we talked about family, too. B.J. had two married boys. He and his wife were separated, but not divorced. He admitted to spending time at their home and alluded to his wife's fragile state and neediness. In a roundabout way, he inferred there was an addiction problem with his eldest son that had taken a toll on his wife. She demanded perfection. I didn't press him with questions and figured he'd tell me more in his own time.

Ours was an old-fashioned and charming courtship that developed over six months before intimacy took us to another level. Building that climax made all the difference among any of my previous relationships where, too often, immediate gratification had won out. What I learned from B.J. was about the rewards of getting to know someone intimately over time. I mean, being allowed to understand the inner workings of someone's brain, heart and experiences, what really makes them tick, and in the organic way we did, leads to the most erotic connection one can know. We were choreographed by nature and at times it was difficult to discern where he ended and I began. Our synergistic understanding of each other made all of our interactions—physical, mental and emotional—an effortless, symbiotic ebb and flow. My Tavern friend Chrissy taught me that yin and yang are equal parts of the same circle. For sure, the way B.J. and I experienced each other was unmatched at that time in my life, and I'm pretty certain he'd say the same. Even strangers commented on our energy field when we walked into a room together.

B.J. was romantic. He'd write me little poems on the back of his drink check when sitting at my bar on Monday nights waiting for me to finish work. He once surprised me with a new stereo and pre-loaded the 5-CD changer with Sade's *Essentials*, *The Best of Anita Baker*, Andrea Bocelli's *Romanza*, Marvin Gaye's *Let's Get It On*, and Sinatra's *Songs for Swingin' Lovers*. One day, I arrived home from the bank and found a copy of *The Bridges of Madison County*, one of his favorite books, wrapped in newspaper in my mailbox. Inside the cover in boyish penmanship and blue ink, he jotted:

V, Same story, different ending. –B.J.

We started to travel occasionally on weekends on little getaways to Annapolis, New York and Fort Lauderdale when I could break away from the Tavern. Threats of a two-table station punishment no longer deterred me from taking off occasionally, now that I had solid footing in my marketing-communications career. We had our regular dinner spots in Philly, too. B.J. was a creature of habit and liked to frequent the same five restaurants where he was known...and made a fuss over. He didn't enjoy checking out the trendiest new places or venturing outside of his comfort zone. And he loved staying overnight at my tiny row home in South Philly because it reminded him of his childhood home, versus the guest suite efficiency he occupied in his office building.

One day, B.J. spontaneously swung by the bank and called me from the car. "Can you sneak out for a little while?" he asked. As the head of my department, I had some autonomy. Still, I felt mischievous, like cutting school. He had a brand new '97 Cadillac Catera that smelled deliciously of leather with the first car phone I had ever seen installed on the center console.

We kissed hello softly on the lips when I got into the car. Time usually stood still for that.

"What's up?" I asked.

"I want to take you somewhere," he said covertly. I had the impression he had something pressing he wanted to talk about, and he did. We drove up the East River Drive past Boathouse Row and continued west on the Schuylkill Expressway. Eventually, B.J. pulled into Valley Forge National Historical Park. We walked about a half mile into the rolling green past Revolutionary monuments to a bench where we sat down. He rested his head on my lap. He was uncharacteristically supine and vulnerable. It was there when B.J. told me two very critical things that would change the trajectory of our lives. One was that he was in love with me. *That was undeniable.* I felt it, too. He looked up at me with surrender in his gray eyes and said, "I've never met anyone like you in my life." He meant it.

The other was that his separation from his wife was not intended as a road to divorce. It was a temporary agreement they had reached, borne of incessant bickering over how to handle family problems, money, houses, etc. that had created a miserable existence for them. They also had been together since the age of nineteen and were clearly mismatched. B.J. hardly knew her when they married. Yet, he felt a strong familial obligation besides an egocentric reputation to uphold among peers and associates. The separation was a needed break from each other, and it was kept under wraps from her country club pals while swearing their kids into secrecy as well. Their separation agreement did not include seeing other people. They had made a pact.

All of a sudden my brain flooded with past conversations and rising blood pressure. I instantaneously replayed B.J.'s reasoning for frequenting only certain restaurants, his preference for sleeping at my place, the long courtship…and at the same time, I felt panic. It was too late. I loved him like I had never loved a man.

"There's more," he added in a low voice.

Uh oh, I thought and tensed to prepare for the incoming blow.

His voice cracked, "She's threatening me constantly. I have to move back into the house."

"Wow," was all I could muster. We sat in silence for a long time and in that silent language we communicated a deeply felt grief for something that had not yet died.

I had been living moment to moment, not worrying about a future I knew would take care of itself. The possibility of not ending up together seemed an impossibility. *What about the message he wrote inside of* Bridges? I questioned. *Why would any adult be so selfish and irresponsible with my feelings as to promise something they knew they couldn't deliver!* And finally, *How could I have missed this through all of my Tavern experiences?* I believe I "missed" it because it was real.

Several days went by without talking. There was a mutually understood period of contemplation about where we would go from there.

Could I remain alone on holidays and dateless at weddings for the rest of my life, giving up the notion of having children, too, in exchange for complete compatibility, operating as one mind, and soulful passion? There it was—my paradox with commitment slapping me straight across the face. It was clear that being alone was a part of either equation. When one half of a perfect couple belongs to someone else, albeit on paper, the other half could never be whole.

The exit signs were all flashing in red.

PINS AND NEEDLES

It had been two months since I had seen B.J., barring one night about a week after our ride to Valley Forge Park when he came over to talk. There was no talking. There were still no words. Instead, we succumbed to the physical yearning for each other and spent the night in my bed.

I was so contemplative that it was difficult to concentrate at work during the day. As a result, I was completely taken by surprise when my boss called me into his office to tell me I was being promoted to vice president. The only person I really wanted to share my news with was B.J., but I couldn't. Until I figured out how I was going to move forward, I kept away. As always, August and Elaina were unconditionally supportive listeners. August was my roommate for a short time during my relationship with B.J. so she experienced us together. She'd often say, "Val, you've met your match." *Hmm.*

I needed something to quell my anxiety and inner turmoil. I was uncomfortable in my own skin, as they say. Ever since being Chrissy's test dummy, AKA a simulated patient during acupuncture school, I had developed a deep appreciation for the modality and its ability to treat physical as well as emotional ails. It was my drug of choice, and I needed a real fix. I grabbed my portable phone and I called Chrissy.

Looking at billowy white clouds painted on the lavender

ceiling above me, I was nearly catatonic. I felt pinned, ironically, to the padded table I laid on. The office was shared with an esthetician in a small, professional building a few blocks from the Tavern. Chrissy came back into the room after about forty minutes to turn my needles and check my pulses. Even while layered with a sweater beneath her lab coat, she was still skinny. Her blue schoolboy glasses framed her big, almond eyes well and added a splash of color to her ivory complexion.

"How do you feel?" she checked in while gently adjusting a few of the needles.

"Really relaxed."

Acupuncturists are trained in reading pulses beyond what Western medicine uses them to measure. Each of the body's major organs has a pulse of its own. In Chinese medicine, when an organ registers a "slow" or "slippery" or otherwise unusual pulse, it tells the acupuncturist, in part, which points require needling to release the obstruction of the flow of energy along the meridians to that organ. Each organ also correlates to our emotional well-being in a particular way. Chrissy was a great five-elemental acupuncture diagnostician. She also knew my story.

"What's the needle in my forearm for?" I wanted to know.

"It treats the pericardium," she answered. Chrissy always talked to me as if I was one of her colleagues. When she wore her white coat, she was fully engaged. I followed along fairly well as she'd provide explanations from a Chinese medicine perspective. After all, I felt like I attended acupuncture school right along with her due to visiting so frequently as her dummy patient. I was also genuinely intrigued by the magic of the electromagnetic movement of *chi*—energy—and completely sold by the ever so subtle, yet undeniable healing I experienced from it.

"The pericardium," Chrissy explained, "is a sack that surrounds the heart. It takes initial trauma directed at the heart, be it physical or emotional, creating a protective barrier."

"As in, a broken heart?" I interrupted.

"Yes, at times," she nodded compassionately. "The pericardium can also aid in balancing the emotions and integrating the heart and mind in sexual relationships," she explained.

A few tears escaped the corners of my closed eyes, rolled behind my ears and landed on the white protective tissue paper covering the treatment bed.

"There's more," Chrissy described. "The heart, pericardium and liver are most closely involved in the emotional life of the human being. Symbolically speaking, the pericardium relates to letting go and moving on. Besides literally moving on, one could also translate that as letting go of the need for permanence. In a relationship, it can allow one to enjoy the relationship in the present moment."

"So, what you're saying is, by letting go of the perceptions we hold about what a relationship is supposed to be, we can live more fully in the present with no attachment to the outcome. Wow! This is almost too much to absorb."

"Turn over onto your stomach," she instructed. Chrissy steadied her hand to needle one last point below the base of my neck called "The Great Hammer," which can be used to break up old, stuck patterns and help one move forward, be it emotional or physical, like having a cold.

While lying face down and internalizing the notion of living in the present, not to mention mentally volleying the riddle of right versus wrong, Chrissy began to tell me a random story about a dog she treated the week before. She was also certified in animal acupuncture. She was wicked smart.

"Hey, did I tell you about the woman up my street who rescues dogs?" she posed.

"Helen, right?"

"Yes," Chrissy affirmed. "She brought a beautiful lab mix into the office for treatment last week. She found the dog lying down under the I-95 and it was covered in fleas. She gave him a flea bath before bringing the dog to see me. His skin was irritated and he was so uncomfortable. Poor doggie. Anyway, Helen said the treatment I gave him helped and it seems to have gotten rid of the fleas. So, if you know anyone who's looking to adopt, let me know."

"What points did you needle on the dog?" I pressed, making idle yet curious conversation.

"Funny you should ask that. The main one is called GV-14 or Governing Vessel. On humans, it's The Great Hammer."

"Oh my God," I muttered to myself aloud. "*Lying dogs.*"

"What did you say?" Chrissy tried to follow my revelation.

"Nothing," I dismissed. "I was just thinking out loud about my life."

I was a little lightheaded from the treatment when I sat up, and perhaps the gravity of my revelation, too. Maybe my grandmothers knew a little something more than I had given them credit for. About twenty minutes later, I grabbed my jacket and was heading toward the front door of the waiting room when I remembered about Friday's lunch plans. Chrissy was there waiting to lock up.

"Chris, are you free Friday afternoon?"

"I think so. Why?" she responded, bending to pick up some mail on the floor by the door.

"Would you like to join Rachael, Ivy and me for lunch at Rosie's?" I suggested. "I've taken the day off from the bank to pick up my new car and we're meeting there around noon."

"Yes, definitely!" she confirmed. Chrissy loved to eat. God bless her.

"Great! I'll see you there, and thank you for the treatment," I acknowledged graciously, giving a little head bow to my healer.

"Don't forget to drink a lot of water today," her voice trailed as I left the office.

One Door Closes

I stood before the large nude woman looking down at me from her chaise on the oil painting on the stairwell wall. Bathed in a spectrum of sun rays streaming into the Tavern through the stained-glass window behind me, the present moment was especially highlighted.

Oh, Anne. I've become you. How did this happen? Have you ever come to this crossroad? What did you do?

I desperately wanted her to step off the canvas and tell me her story. I wanted to know the ending. Instead, the words of wisdom handed down from my female lineage once again ran across my brain like a screensaver on a PC. They streamed, "Remember, as one door closes another one opens. Give away the milk and no one will buy the cow. The show must go on."

Shut up already!

Cap interrupted my thoughts. "Val, there's an envelope on the bar with your name on it. Someone left it there before I got here," he informed me.

"Okay, thanks, Cap." I headed over to the bar to start setting up. I saw the white, #10 business envelope sitting by the cash register. I recognized the boyish penmanship that spelled "Val" on the outside from many a cryptogram, and tucked the envelope into my handbag. I was not in the right frame of mind to read it and instead turned my attention to cutting a dozen limes and lemons into quarters, filling the maraschino cherries well, making lemon twists with a potato peeler, and counting my cash drawer. These were mindless tasks that allowed me to appear busy while my mind chattered on. *Was there a letter in the envelope with a plea I couldn't turn down?* I remained disciplined, strengthened by a desire to avoid any possible threat of manipulation because, inside, I knew exactly what I needed to do. I also knew it was not going to be easy, and for a while, I would feel empty, pulseless and directionless. *That would be okay,* I thought with conviction. *I had some experience with heartbreak and eventually emerged on the other side, which invariably holds better, yet perhaps preordained, possibilities.*

Midway through the evening, with a bar full of first-date couples, a few regulars, and a group of drunk obnoxious businessmen (more like slobbery dogs making nauseating, flirtatious comments to me whenever I replenished their drinks), I kept thinking about opening the envelope.

A newer, young server appeared at the service end of the bar. She needed a bottle of Ruffino for Table 5. As I was removing the tin cover from the bottle top with the blade on my wine key, one of the intoxicated idiots bellowed from the end of the bar, "Hey, Tits, could you get me another gin and tonic?" That term was only acceptable from the men I worked with at the Tavern who actually respected me. Time stopped for a minute. My heart rate increased. For a split second, I wanted to pass along some sage wisdom by way of sarcasm to the college girl standing before me waiting for Table 5's bottle of wine.

Instead, in one fluid motion, still holding the bottle of Ducale in my left hand, I reached under the shelf, grabbed my leather jacket and handbag, and ducked out from beneath the service bar counter. I walked toward the group of businessmen and placed the bottle of wine on the bar in front of them.

"Here, help yourselves to this."

I hurriedly walked out the front door toward my Protege up the street, dropping my server pouch to the sidewalk. I wanted to drive away as quickly as possible before Cap could realize I was gone…and encourage me to stay, or at least to finish the shift. I got into the car and pulled out. On autopilot, I drove a few blocks in the opposite direction of home and parked in the first open spot I found on 9th Street near Spruce. I took the envelope out of my bag and opened it. Inside was a Tavern bar napkin with a message impressed on it in blue ink:

> To Val:
> It's better to have Valerie'd and lost than never to
> have Valerie'd at all. I borrowed this from
> Richard Burton. Hope you don't mind. These
> are the only words I can conjure at the moment
> to truly say how I feel…a little lost and forever
> changed.
> Love Always,
> B.J.

I put the napkin back inside the #10 envelope B.J. left for me at the bar. I sat in my car for a long time thinking about a possible response. In complete departure from the conventional behavior exhibited by men having affairs as I observed countless times at the Tavern, I knew B.J. was actually being *un*selfish by letting me go. He would never expect me to settle for the sidelines. I'm really not sure how long I sat there. Finally, I decided that the silent language would convey my speechlessness far more powerfully than any words I could invoke. I looked up through my windshield and noticed a public garbage can sitting a few feet from my car. *Perfect*. I didn't need to hold on to B.J.'s note as a memento of our relationship. I already had everything I needed.

The conclusion to my relationship with B.J. left me a little scathed in that I was certain I could never replicate those exact feelings. Truthfully, I didn't want to because I liked having them tucked into the special place they occupied in my pericardium.

The conclusion to my relationship with the Tavern left me irrefutably changed in more ways than I can articulate. The experiences, intimacies and friendships I acquired there made me smarter, a little jaded, worldlier, funnier, less rigid, more introspective, a veritable expert in human behavior, and a lot closer to dropping my "Co-D" bag.

Well, my grandmothers were certainly right about fleas! But, nothing a little Mexican "repelente" or a good acupuncture treatment couldn't release, all things considered. Given the chance, I probably wouldn't change too much, and especially not the adventures.

The Tavern women I met and worked with were a smorgasbord: we were from various towns and states, cultural and religious backgrounds, and an assortment of family dynamics, not to mention the diversity in our appearances and careers. Yet we all shared two fundamental qualities for sure: resourcefulness and humor. This allowed us to continue working at the Tavern far longer than expected, to keep our eyes on the prize and to roll with the punches. It seems in jobs where there is great adrenaline output, like a fast-paced restaurant, fraternity and release are inherent.

My mother always said, "Show me your friends and I'll tell you who you are."

Any time, mom. Any time.

To Natalie —

OK already,
So where the hell
were you? We
waited + waited —
But you never showed up!
Anyway, I missed you
you again —
Dammit!
love Billy Joel

Acknowledgments

Thanks to my mom, Rita Pantaleo, who taught me how to laugh, and to my dad, Dominic Pantaleo, who taught me how to be funny. *Dad, you were the best storyteller ever! I hope you're still at it...somewhere out there.*

To my sisters, Cheryl, Steph, and Pam for sharing a lifetime of experiences with me and helping frame my perspective. A special thanks to Pam for her intelligent editing suggestions on the earliest version of this book over a decade ago. Speaking of way back—thanks, Craig, for keeping Madi occupied during my very first attempts at "writing this down."

To Kim and Linda, my sisters not by blood but by choice, I can hardly conjure a memory that doesn't include one or both of you, going back to five years old with Kim! You are among my life's blessings. It's safe to say I'll probably never catch up in hours served listening. *Sorry, I chose the path of adventure...and risk.* I thank you for being the best supporting characters any friend, or author, could ask for. To Maria Di., for your lifelong friendship, not to mention singing Billy Joel songs as we made our way down the boardwalk from Morey's Pier, and to Donna S. for your angelic voice of calm. You all live inside my heart.

To Mark—without you, it's likely no one would be holding this book in their hands. Thank you for taking me to Sedona. Thank you for believing in me, for your encouragement and all the support you provided that made turning a draft manuscript into a tangible reality and the fulfillment of a dream.

A special thanks to a few other supporting characters: Ronnie and Joe, for the many birthday dinners, B.J. concerts, and helping to create memories beyond your cameos here. Thank you Donna R. for your creativity and friendship, and to Lorraine R. for your solid support personally and professionally. Additional thanks to one of my early mentors and sources of inspiration, Bill Tonelli.

To my beloved, late Uncle Frank: the world can finally read some of your beautiful words in a small way. To Aunt Nina (*one of my earliest beta reviewers!*) and Uncle Joe B. for summers at the shore. To my dear, departed Aunt Angela, thank you for your unconditional love and wisdom, and to my late Uncle Vince for sharing many funny experiences. To my late Aunt Mary who had the most contagious laugh, and Uncle Joe C.—I hope to have half your memory at your age. And, to my late Great-Aunt Vi and Uncle Tony who personified "the greatest generation"…you've all helped raise me.

To Lindsay Allison Dierking, my gifted editor and publisher, thank you for the gentle yet wise guidance you provided throughout this publishing journey. Even more, I'm so very grateful the fates (and Paula Petrovic) brought us together in the 3D, and for the brilliant light you shine in the lives of everyone lucky enough to come into your orbit. Thank you, Kurt, for your talent, insight, and awesome designs.

To my dear friend Iris especially, for inspiring me to "write this down," and for your wisdom, memories, support, networking, and sisterhood. To Richie, Frani, Robin, my acupuncture guru and close friend Cathy, Christina, Amy, Christian, Sandee, Rosalie, Paula, Joey P., Rose, Patty, Sandy, Sally, Cindy, Heidi, Kim, Julie, Lisa, Denise, Benny (RIP), Jules (RIP), Big Bobby (RIP), Charlie (RIP), Maria M., Tucker, Dawn, Michael A., Anne, Frank R., Susan, Dr.

Frank, Larry, Maria D., Ronnie, JuJu, Donna, Nita, Cory (RIP), Chrissy, Maggie, Stephanie, Mark S., Deanna, Libby, Mara, Ray, Vanessa, Maria L., Lynnie, Mikey A., Billy, Eddie K., Cousin Joe P., George L., George W., Harry (RIP), Noel (RIP), Baby Binns (RIP), Anthony, Eddie, Harvey (RIP), LC (RIP), Tommy, Mike, and especially Big Jim who each played a part in my story and moved me to write it. Thanks to all the other characters here and gone I may have missed who inspired these and countless untold anecdotes.

Thanks to Bobbi Hyman for sharing your talent and the beautiful paintings of strong women, one of whom graces the cover of this book.

And to Billy Joel—thanks for the music, man, and the note I still have in a photo album.

About Natalie

Natalie Pantaleo is a Philadelphia-based marketing-communications consultant, consummate storyteller, and first-time book author with *Lying Down with Dogs*. As early as the caption in her eighth-grade yearbook indicates, Natalie has wanted to write for a living, and that she does...and more.

Adept at interpreting complex information, Natalie creates digestible, well-positioned and compelling content and campaigns for targeted audiences. She is a published features writer and an innovative thinking facilitator as well. Her resume spans healthcare, finance, non-profit, education, and retail. A seasoned strategist, she's led teams at First Penn Bank, Franklin Mint Federal Credit Union, DSC Advertising, and the National Board of Osteopathic Medical Examiners. More recently, Natalie's guided clients like New York's

Hudson Bread, Los Angeles-based Josie Maran Cosmetics and Revmo, Inc. in Las Vegas. In 2021, Natalie launched her website: **www.TheInsideOutMarketer.com**.

Like *Lying Down with Dogs*' protagonist, Valerie, Natalie attributes her ability to capture nuance, her fundamental sense of humor and the witty side of sarcasm to her colorful upbringing in the subculture of South Philadelphia where Italian American influence provided anecdotes for life. "South Philly follows me wherever I go, and I wouldn't have it any other way," Natalie admits.

She holds an M.A. in Bilingual/Bi-Cultural Studies of Spanish from LaSalle University where she graduated with honors, and a B.A. in Journalism and Public Relations from Temple University. She joyfully contributed time and talent to the Leukemia Society, Cystic Fibrosis and Alexsandra Bilotti foundations. Among her endeavors, Natalie says her most creative and enlightening work-in-progress is raising her lovely and spirited teenage daughter, Madi.

CPSIA information can be obtained
at www.ICGtesting.com
Printed in the USA
BVHW070520141222
654166BV00001B/6